LAND WARFARE
Brassey's New Battlefield Weapons Systems and Technology Series
into the 21st Century

Volume 4

SURVEILLANCE AND TARGET ACQUISITION SYSTEMS

Second Edition

LAND WARFARE
Brassey's New Battlefield Weapons Systems and Technology Series
into the 21st Century

Editor-in-Chief: Colonel R G Lee OBE, Former Military Director of Studies,
Royal Military College of Science, Shrivenham, UK.

The success of the first and second series on Battlefield Weapons Systems and Technology
and the pace of advances in military technology have prompted Brassey's to produce a
new Land Warfare Series. This series updates subjects covered in the original series, and
also covers completely new areas. The new books are written for military personnel who
wish to advance their professional knowledge. In addition, they are intended to aid
anyone who is interested in the design, development and production of military
equipment.

Series 3

Volume 1 **Military Ballistics: A Basic Manual** – G M Moss, D W Leeming and C L Farrar

Volume 2 **Cannons** – D F Allsop

Volume 3 **Guns, Mortars and Rockets, Revised Edition** – M P Manson

Volume 4 **Surveillance and Target Acquisition Systems, Second Edition** –
M A Richardson *et al*

Volume 5 **Guided Weapons, Third Edition** – R G Lee *et al*

Volume 6 **Small Arms and Machine-Guns** – D F Allsop and M A Toomey

Volume 7 **Explosives, Propellants and Pyrotechnics, Second Edition** – A Bailey and
S G Murray

SURVEILLANCE AND TARGET ACQUISITION SYSTEMS

Second Edition

● ● ● ● ● ● ● ●

M A Richardson, I C Luckraft, R S Picton, A L Rodgers and R F Powell

Royal Military College of Science, Shrivenham, UK

BRASSEY'S
London · Washington

First English Edition 1983
Second Revised Edition 1997

UK editorial offices: Brassey's, 33 John Street, London WC1N 2AT
Tel: 0171 753 7777 Fax: 0171 753 7794
Email: brasseys@dial.pipex.com Web: http://www.brasseys.com
UK orders: Marston Book Services, PO Box 269, Abingdon, OX14 4SD

North American orders: Brassey's Inc., 22883 Quicksilver Drive,
Sterling, VA 20166, USA

M A Richardson, I C Luckraft, R S Picton, A L Rodgers and R F Powell
have asserted their moral right to be identified as the authors of this work.

Library of Congress Cataloging in Publication Data
available

British Library Cataloguing in Publication Data

A Catalogue record for this book is available from the British Library

ISBN 1 85753 137 X hardcover

The front cover shows The 'Maxi-Kite' intensified sight (*photo courtesy of Pilkington Optronics*)

The title pages show the Rapier Air Defence System Alerting Radar (*photo courtesy of British Aerospace*)

Typeset by M Rules in Stone Serif
Printed in Great Britain by Redwood Books, Trowbridge

Preface

THE SERIES

This series of books is written for those who wish to improve their knowledge of military weapons and equipment. It is equally relevant to professional soldiers, those involved in developing or producing military weapons or indeed anyone interested in the art of modern warfare.

All the texts are written in a way which assumes no mathematical knowledge and no more technical depth than would be gleaned from school days. It is intended that the books should be of particular interest to army officers who are studying for promotion examinations, furthering their knowledge at specialist arms schools or attending command and staff schools.

The authors of the books are all members of the staff of the Royal Military College of Science, Shrivenham, which is comprised of a unique blend of academic and military experts. They are not only leaders in the technology of their subjects, but are aware of what the military practitioner needs to know. It is difficult to imagine any group of persons more fitted to write about the application of technology to the battlefield.

VOLUME IV

The ability to carry out surveillance and acquire targets has taken great steps forward in recent years. This second edition has been extensively rewritten and totally updated, such that the reader will become aware of the latest techniques used for surveillance and target acquisition systems in the fields of electro-optics, radar and acoustics. The volume also encompasses the use of these techniques, and countermeasures to them, in the context of the modern battlefield.

Geoffrey Lee, Shrivenham

Acknowledgements

The editor would like to express his thanks to the authors of the first edition of this text and hopes that this second edition meets with their approval. Many thanks to Andrew Figgures for the significant groundwork he undertook in getting this edition started. Thanks also to the many friends and colleagues at Shrivenham, especially Nick Smith, Charles Kirke, Bill McCluggage and Mike Thurbon for their valued comments, and to Ken Thomas for his inspiration. Thanks must also go to Julie Sharp for her excellent graphics, and Julie Bint and Kathryn Noon for their help with the typing of the manuscript.

Mark Richardson
Shrivenham, February 1997

Contents

List of Illustrations

1

••••••••

Introduction

SCOPE

Surveillance and target acquisition (STA) are fundamental to the prosecution of war in all dimensions. The capability to achieve surveillance or target acquisition or indeed defeat that capability in others has a powerful impact on the characteristics and conduct of operations. Surprise, tempo, the manoeuvre of mass and extent of operations are dependent upon STA capabilities. The result of STA is information, information that can be analysed to produce combat intelligence or to bring a weapon to bear; hence surveillance and target acquisition are linked closely to information technology both with respect to processing and dissemination. The miniaturisation of electronics which proceeds apace has already had significant effects on surveillance and target acquisition such that the nature of war is being transformed. Vast amounts of information are produced and passed by more capable communications. This, if not processed and dealt with correctly, could make the tasks of commanders, staffs and weapon crews more difficult by them becoming overloaded with the sheer quantity of the information available. It also makes the dividends to be gained from deception and degradation of STA capabilities much greater. Therefore from the statement of the requirement to the acceptance of the surveillance and target acquisition equipment one must always consider that it will not operate in isolation. It is but part of a greater system. Consequently its operation must be consistent with our own military doctrine and take account of a potential enemy's reaction.

This chapter defines what is meant by surveillance and target acquisition in a military sense, it describes how the requirements to achieve an appropriate capability are arrived at and outlines the technologies that can be used to meet it.

In subsequent chapters these technologies, electro-optics and radar are explored in more depth. The scientific and engineering principles which underpin the application of electro-optics and radar are described together with their capabilities and constraints. The aim being that the reader should recognise and have some appreciation of the factors that determine the design, selection and performance of current surveillance and target acquisition systems.

DEFINITIONS

There are many definitions of surveillance but in the context of the battlefield the following is perhaps the most useful.

> Surveillance is the continuous systematic watch over the battlefield area to provide timely information for combat intelligence.

To be effective the watch must be continuous. Systems therefore must have a day and night capability. They must operate in all weathers, including haze, mist, cloud, rain and snow. They must be effective under battlefield conditions such as smoke and dust. In addition to being continuous the watch must be systematic so that the whole area of interest is covered without interruption; or, if this is not possible, the whole area of interest should be scanned or revisited with the appropriate frequency to allow the updating of information as necessary. Finally, the information must be timely to allow the appropriate reaction. Analysis of information to provide combat intelligence takes time as does its dissemination. This combined with planning, the issuing of orders and executing the necessary deployment further contributes to the response time. This response time varies with the level of command: a section can react more swiftly than an army group. Hence the concept of an area of interest.

The area of interest is understood to be that area of concern to the commander. This includes the area in which he is capable of directly influencing operations by manoeuvre and the direct or indirect fire systems which are normally under his control, and the area adjacent on the flanks and extending forward to the objectives of current or future operations. This also includes areas occupied or which could be occupied by enemy forces that might affect the outcome or jeopardise his current or future operations. These areas are often shown in terms of distance for a linear deployment. This may be misleading; they should be thought of with respect to time and space, for the area of interest is dependent upon the mobility of the enemy's and one's own forces. Clearly there will be overlap of areas of interest between formations. Surveillance and hence the gathering of combat intelligence is co-ordinated by allocating areas of intelligence responsibility, that is the area in which a commander at any level is responsible for intelligence and hence surveillance. The size of an area of intelligence responsibility at any level is a function of the surveillance capability available to the commander. The area of interest is an important factor in establishing the range requirement of surveillance systems to be used at any level of command. Hence with the advent of greater dispersion and a less dense deployment of forces the range and area coverage required of surveillance systems is increased.

Target acquisition is defined as the detection, recognition, identification and location of a target in sufficient detail to permit the effective deployment of weapons.

The range at which this can be achieved is a limiting factor in determining the effective range of a weapon. Hence the procurement of a long-range weapon system must also be accompanied by a complementary target acquisition system, otherwise the long range cannot be fully exploited.

Detection is the discovery by any means of the presence of something of potential military interest. It may be an object or phenomenon such as a radio signal or laser beam. It is brought about because of a contrast, some discontinuity or a movement between the target and its background. Very little information about the target is required to alert the observer or sensor. Its importance in the target acquisition sequence is that it focuses attention on the area or cues a system with better resolution.

Recognition is the classification of the object of potential military interest by its appearance or behaviour. The shape of the object and, in particular, if it has a gun, turret, tracks or wheels enables it to be classified as a main battle tank (MBT), self-propelled (SP) gun, armoured personnel carrier (APC) or wheeled vehicle. The behaviour of the target is also an aid to recognition. Its manner and direction of movement or the elevation of its gun are indicators of its purpose. It may have to be observed for some time before a discernible pattern of behaviour emerges.

Identification is the stage in the acquisition process in which the target is established as being friend or foe and its type. Although the characteristic features of a target, its running gear or fume extractor for example, may indicate its nationality and distinguish it from all others of its class, they are often minor and easily obscured. Hence to achieve identification demands the capability to determine much more detail than recognition.

Identification can be eased by the display of a recognisable feature such as a call sign plate or air recognition sign. If an overt form of identification is used it should be identifiable by all sensors used by one's own side. Any overt system is, of course, going to draw the enemy's attention to the equipment, hence covert methods of identification have been developed ranging from the audible (such as passwords), visual (using prearranged signals such as flares), or electronic (as used in identification friend or foe – IFF – systems employed in many air defence systems).

Location is the determination of a target's position with sufficient accuracy with respect to the weapons system to allow a successful engagement. The amount of information required to successfully locate a target is dependent upon the range and type of weapon system used. The requirements for direct fire, indirect fire and guided weapon systems vary.

A direct-fire system requires azimuth and elevation to the target. The former is easily obtained by aligning the bore of the weapon with the target. The accuracy necessary for this is dependent upon range and target size. A pistol can be pointed, a tank gun requires a complex optical sight to lay the gun on the target. Elevation is more complex since it is range dependent for all direct-fire weapons with the possible exception of high-velocity weapons at short range. There are a variety of range determining techniques that may be used.

Visual estimation with or without a map is largely dependent upon the experience and eyesight of the user. Stadiametric rangefinders use a graticule pattern to determine the range of a target of known height or width. Such a system is often used as a reversionary mode in tank gunnery.

Ranging rounds either from the main armament or from a smaller-calibre, coaxially-mounted weapon are relatively cheap and effective but slow. Optical rangefinders, such as the stereoscopic and coincidence variety are effective but complex. Radar, while important in its own right as a surveillance system, may also be used to provide accurate location and range information and so track targets. It is often used for the fire-control system for anti-aircraft guns. The laser rangefinder is, however, the principle range-finding system employed today, being both accurate and easy to use.

For indirect-fire systems the problem of location is complicated by the absence of a line of sight between the weapon and the target. The target has therefore to be acquired by an observer, remote from the weapon system, who can either estimate the grid reference and elevation of the target or, knowing his own location, measure the bearing and range to the target and pass the information to the gun position or base plate. This can then be compared with the location of the weapon and the necessary elevation and azimuth calculated. It is highly desirable to achieve first-round accuracy as this will be more effective than adjusting fire on to the target. To achieve this the observer needs to be able to measure the range to the target accurately, with, for example, a laser rangefinder and to determine accurately the azimuth and elevation or depression of the target with respect to his location. Hence the requirement for an angulation head upon which to mount the rangefinder. The observer and the weapon system must also find their location either by survey or from some form of position determining system.

The accuracy of the location of a target for a guided weapon system depends upon the system of guidance used. At one end of the scale there is the relatively simple requirement to be able to lay the sight of the weapon on to the target and allow the missile to be guided until impact. Provided the target is within range of the missile, for example in an anti-tank system, its exact determination is not critical. At the other extreme there is a high degree of location accuracy necessary to allow a target such as a fast aircraft or missile to be hit.

It is not necessary to go through all the four stages of target acquisition to engage a target. Location is essential, and depending upon the degree of risk or uncertainty acceptable in the engagement, either detection, recognition or identification is also required. Detection alone will seldom suffice but recognition may often be adequate when it is known, for example, that there are no friendly tanks in an area and therefore a tank seen there can be assumed to be hostile.

The degree of detail required increases with each stage of the target acquisition sequence. Thus a higher performance system is needed to achieve identification at a given range rather than, say recognition. Conversely, for a given system the range at which identification will be achieved will be less than that for recognition, which will, in turn, be less than that for detection.

TECHNIQUES USED IN SURVEILLANCE AND TARGET ACQUISITION

A target reveals its presence because of its physical or chemical characteristics. These characteristics can be detected by the human senses, sight and hearing being the most important. For example, a tank is recognised from its shape and the observer's attention may have first been attracted by the noise of its engine, transmission and running gear. Human vision has its limitations particularly at night and in poor weather. In addition, its performance deteriorates with range. Hence the drive to enhance the senses and enable them to exploit physical and chemical characteristics which are not capable of human detection without the assistance of technology. The techniques which enhance or enable the senses to exploit otherwise undetectable characteristics may be classified in three groups, as shown in Figure 1.1.

- Electromagnetic energy such as light or radio waves.
- Sound or vibration known as mechanical waves.
- Other target effects such as smell.

By far the most widely used techniques for detecting targets are those that exploit electromagnetic (EM) energy or radiation. This EM energy may be natural as in sunlight or artificial as in electric light. Visible radiation is detected by the eye after reflection, sometimes with the aid of binoculars or sights. There is also considerable reflection in the near infra-red (IR) portion of the spectrum which

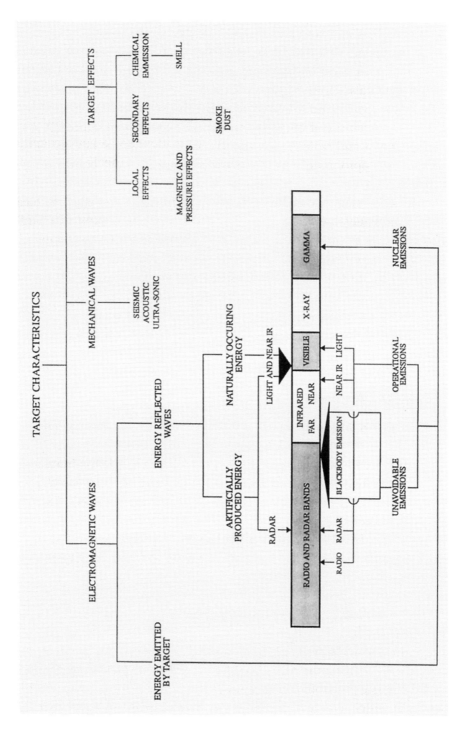

Figure 1.1 The Search for Information and Targets

can be detected and converted into a visual image by image intensifiers (II) or low-light television (LLTV). Targets may also emit EM energy over a wide range of frequencies. This emission can be unavoidable or deliberate. Unavoidable emissions are dependent upon the temperature of the target and are known as black-body radiation. Most of the energy is in the far IR portion of the spectrum, but some energy is also emitted in the microwave region. IR radiation is detected by thermal imaging (TI) and infra-red line scan (IRLS) systems.

Deliberate or operational emissions arise from spot lights, flares, IR search lights, lasers, radars and radio. These operational emissions can be detected and by means of an appropriate sensor array the location of the emitter may be determined.

Although electromagnetic radiation is the most frequent and effective means of detection, considerable effort has been invested in exploiting mechanical waves. Vibration or seismic waves caused by vehicles or soldiers can be detected by sensors remotely embedded in the ground. Sound or acoustic waves caused by helicopters or the firing of guns can be detected by microphones and the source located. At sea acoustic and ultrasonic waves are utilised in sonar systems.

Other target effects such as chemical emissions are particularly useful when exploited by sniffer devices or dogs to detect arms, explosives, men and chemical agents.

ACTIVE AND PASSIVE SYSTEMS

All the techniques mentioned above may be classified as active or passive.

Active systems are those which radiate energy at the target to illuminate it. The use of an active system can be detected by the target and often reveals the position of the sensor. They are therefore vulnerable to countermeasures. Examples of active systems are radars, lasers and searchlights.

Passive systems do not rely on the radiation of energy generated by the observer. They therefore consume less power and are less likely to give away the system's location.

FACTORS AFFECTING PERFORMANCE

The performance of a STA system is often quoted as a range. This is meaningless unless one specifies the nature of the target, the conditions prevailing, what is to be achieved and the probability of its being achieved.

The range at which a target is acquired is governed by the physical characteristics of the target upon which the contrast between it and its background depends. In general terms, the higher the level of energy emitted or reflected from the target compared with the background the greater the contrast, hence the greater the range at which it will be seen. Thus the size of the target and its ability to emit or reflect energy are significant factors in determining acquisition range.

Equally, the energy emitted or reflected must contrast with the background in the area of the EM spectrum that the surveillance system operates in. For example, a target which is conspicuous when viewed by a thermal device may be well concealed from visual observation.

The acquisition range for a given target and background may be further degraded by poor light and atmospheric conditions. Poor light reduces the amount of energy that is reflected from a target and its background. This makes it difficult for the eye to see detail and hence the range at which a target can be acquired is reduced. Simple optical instruments, such as weapon sights and binoculars, provide some assistance by reason of their magnification when conditions are good, as in moonlight or at twilight. Their performance in these circumstances, however, does not compare with their capability in daylight. The performance of passive devices which make use of star- and moon-light are also governed by the level of ambient light from these sources.

The performance of all STA devices is affected to some extent by poor weather conditions. Haze, mist, fog, rain and snow absorb or scatter energy reflected or emitted from the target and degrade or obscure the contrast between the target and its background. The effect of atmospheric interference upon surveillance systems is governed by the wavelength at which the system operates. In general, the longer the wavelength the less the performance of the system is reduced. The graphs in Figure 1.2 illustrate the impact of weather on visibility. This shows that visibilities of less than 5km are not likely on average; however, atmospheric interference may be severe in certain areas, for example, over low-lying ground and at certain times of the year, particularly in winter. Vision may also be limited

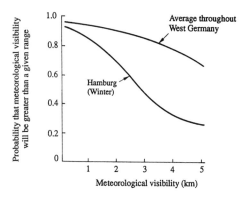

Figure 1.2 Meteorological Visibility in W Germany (Daylight)

by the formation of a mirage brought about by the reflection of the sky caused by the bending of light rays by variations in air density.

A major constraint on performance is the shielding of the target by natural or artificial obstacles such as hills, trees and buildings; in other words, inter-visibility. Inter-visibility is not just being able to see one point from another, for, as was mentioned in the sequence for target acquisition, time is required to study a target to recognise and in particular identify it. The conditions of inter-visibility in north-west Europe are shown in Figure 1.3. Care should be taken in interpreting them, for on inspection there appears less than a 10 per cent chance that a line of sight will exceed 3km, and there is less than a 5 per cent chance that the line of sight will exceed 5km. In the past this has been reason for saying that there is small justification for a 'ground based' line-of-sight surveillance device with acquisition ranges in excess of 5km. This takes no account of requirements in other theatres of operation such as open desert, although the improvement in probability of achieving a greater line of sight in such conditions is not as great as may be expected because of the fact that naturally flat terrain has a certain amount of undulation or roughness which may provide cover for a target.

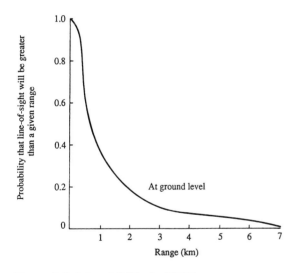

Figure 1.3 Intervisibility in NW Europe

A further constraint on performance is the cost of the system. In general, a more capable system, with the ability to acquire a target at greater range, will be larger and more expensive than a less capable system. One should be cautious of applying the law of diminishing returns when determining the requirement. A cut off at say the 80 per cent point may affect acquisition of only 20 per cent of possible targets. In doing so the assumption has been made that all targets have the same tactical value whenever they are in the direct fire zone. This is not true.

The destruction of these targets at close range is critical to survival for both defender and attacker. The destruction of targets at long range, and the longer the better for the defender, make the attacker react prematurely. If the attacker has the ability to destroy targets by fire at long range then this may prevent the necessity of deployment or reduce the extent of deployment for an assault, hence the momentum and speed of the advance is maintained.

Furthermore, if there is tactical value in longer-range engagements, the design of STA systems must take into account the tendency for exposure times to be shorter at longer range. The ability of an observer to see the extent of dead ground in front of him will vary with the angle of sight, and for a given height difference the angle of sight depends on range. Thus, for example, if an MBT is moving toward an observer its exposure times will be shorter at longer ranges. Therefore to achieve detection, recognition or identification with reduced exposure times requires increased system resolution, and hence a further increase in the cost and complexity of that system.

This illustrates the point that the capability required must not only take into account the terrain but also tactical doctrine. Capability can only be traded against cost and complexity if one is fully aware of the implications when setting up the operational analysis to justify the requirement. It furthermore indicates that when comparing performance or specifying it one has to determine the nature of the acquisition task in terms of exposure time and size of sector in which the target is to be acquired.

Finally, in performance specification or assessment there is bound to be an element of uncertainty, not least in the ability of the individual observer to detect, recognise or identify a particular target. The acceptable success rate must be fixed. As conditions, particularly atmospheric, may vary then one must also fix the probability of success throughout the year. Hence a performance requirement for a STA system might be phrased as follows: 'To achieve a 50 per cent chance of recognition 80 per cent of the year in north-west Europe against a standard tank target moving against a standard background'.

2

·······

Visual Surveillance

INTRODUCTION

Of all the ways of conveying information about a particular environment or situation, images are the most powerful, whether the image is a simple sketch map, an indistinct view through a long-range imager or a full colour photograph. All of them convey to a greater or lesser extent the impression of actually 'being there', and although it is a truism of everyday life that a picture is worth a thousand words, an image does uniquely convey the layout of a particular scene and the nature of the objects within it. In the terms of the previous chapter, it gives the observer not just the ability to detect distant objects, but also the capability to *recognise* or *identify* them. It is not surprising therefore that 75 per cent of the activity in the human brain appears to be associated with the processing of information generated by the visual system.

For the human observer then the eyes are very much the prime sensing system, and much of this book presents technological ways of assisting their performance by 'seeing' at longer ranges or under poorer lighting conditions, or by using parts of the EM system which the eye cannot detect to generate image information.

The fundamental processes involved in imaging surveillance are illustrated in Figure 2.1 below. For daylight imaging, ambient ('background') illumination falls on the objects in the scene and is *diffusely* reflected off to varying degrees, that is to say, it is scattered in all directions. Naturally, some objects reflect more light than others, and it is this which is responsible to a large degree for our being able to pick out distinct objects within the scene. One of the important attributes of objects which may be of interest from the surveillance point of view is thus their *reflectivity*, that is, the proportion of the incoming light that they reflect.

The reflected light then travels through the intervening atmosphere to the observer, where it must be collected and focused into an image and interpreted. Our ability to see the things we need to depends on the several factors associated with each part of this chain of events, from the nature and quantity of light

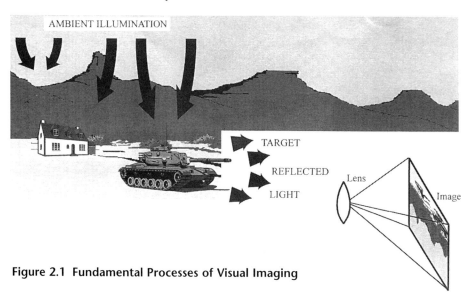

Figure 2.1 Fundamental Processes of Visual Imaging

falling on the scene, the nature of the target and background, atmospheric conditions, to the quality and size of the collection optics, and so on. Understanding surveillance technology thus requires an insight into the processes involved in each one of these steps. On the other hand too, useful implications for counter-surveillance may be drawn from understanding and capitalising on the factors which disrupt the surveillance process.

Scene illumination

By day, the sun provies good illumination over the complete range of wavelengths of EM radiation which are visible to the eye (the *visible spectrum*, which extends from about 0.4µm to about 0.7µm). Figure 2.2 shows the distribution of the energy of sunlight through these wavelengths at the surface of the earth, together with the corresponding distributions for moonlight (which is, of course, reflected sunlight), and starlight. Note that the peak output of the sun occurs at about 0.55µm, which is also the wavelength of light for which the eye is most sensitive (for daylight vision).

By day, there is such good illumination that the eye and many daylight imaging systems can afford to detect light in different parts of the visible spectrum separately, providing us with *colour* information, based on the fact that most objects do not have exactly the same reflectivity at all wavelengths in the visible spectrum. We, like many other creatures, have evolved to make good use of this additional information, giving us a high degree of colour discrimination and with it an enhanced ability to detect and recognise objects in good light.

Useful as this facility is, it does generally demand relatively high light levels, because the separate detection of different parts of the spectrum is inevitably

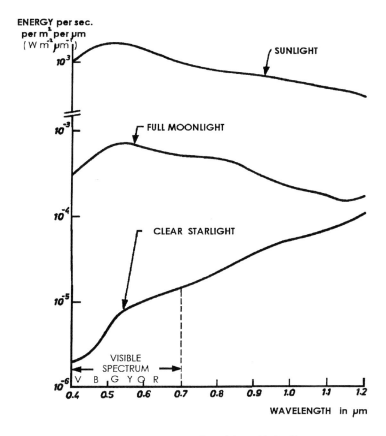

Figure 2.2 Spectral Distribution of Ambient Light Sources

somewhat wasteful; it also increases the complexity (and cost) of sensors, or degrades their performance relative to a similar black and white system. Most military sensing systems which are intended to provide useful imagery over a wide range of conditions thus use monochrome sensors, particularly if they are to be associated with intensifiers, which are inherently monochrome unless incorporated into specialised and complex low-light surveillance systems.

It is also clear from Figure 2.2 that the starlight energy distribution is quite different in nature from sunlight. This is partly for the obvious reason that starlight is produced by a large number of separate and different stars, but also because a substantial proportion of the illumination under these conditions is 'sky glow' due to electrical activity in the upper atmosphere. This fact together with the much lower levels of energy in starlight has important consequences for the types of detector material needed in systems operating under these conditions.

Illuminance and Visual Cues

Because ambient illumination conditions can vary so much, and different types of imaging system require different light levels to operate, it is important to be able to quantify how much light is falling on a surface per unit area. Properly, this quantity is known as *illuminance* (symbol E, and its modern (SI) unit is the *lux* (or for night-time conditions, the millilux, which is one thousandth of a lux). Table 2.1 lists a variety of illumination conditions, together with typical illuminance values for the UK and a rough indication of the performance of the eye under these conditions. It is worth noting, however, that in peacetime in the UK there is often a considerable glow in the sky from distant urban centres (particularly in cloudy conditions), resulting in ambient illuminance values of 10 to 20 millilux even on overcast, moonless nights.

There are a variety of factors which determine whether or not an object in a scene will be seen by an observer, including, for instance, the size of the object and the illumination conditions. From the surveillance point of view, we need to assess and quantify the ease with which objects in the field of view can be detected and recognised. Conversely, from the counter-surveillance stand-point, it is important to understand and hinder the detection and recognition processes. The mechanisms used by the brain for the recognition of specific objects are complex and the subject of much current research, but there are a variety of well-known visual cues which alert the observer to the presence of an object of interest.

As we have seen, objects are visible because they reflect a proportion of the ambient light. Clearly, if an object reflects light very differently from its surroundings, it will be easy to pick out (given enough light for the imaging system to work efficiently). The most fundamental cue is the presence of an identifiable area of the scene with a different 'brightness' to its surroundings, that is, something which *contrasts* with its background. Contrast may be defined in several ways, but it is generally taken as the difference of brightness between an object and its background, expressed as a proportion of some measure of the overall scene brightness.

When both target and background are seen purely by reflection of the same ambient light, contrast arises purely because of a difference between the target and the background reflectivity (using this definition), a fact well-known in the long history of camouflage, where the importance of making objects 'look like' their background has long been recognised. For colour scenes and full colour-imaging systems this is complicated by the fact that the reflection coefficients vary with wavelength, so contrast depends on the particular range of wavelengths of interest. This reflects the everyday experience that objects are particularly easy to pick out if their colours contrast with their environment.

Table 2.1 Illuminance Levels by Day and Night in Lux for United Kingdom

Situation	Level in Lux	Eye Response
clear sunlight (as seen by pilot at 30,000 ft)	10^5	glare
full summer day (noon)	7×10^4	
cloudy summer/bright winter day (noon)	2×10^4	optimum vision
cloudy/dull winter day (noon)	5×10^3	
heavily overcast winter day (noon)	10^3	good vision
good indoor working illumination	5×10^2	
winter sunset (clear sky)	2×10^2	
twilight (dusk	10^1	poor colour and
deep twilight	10^0	detail discrimination
clear moonlight (moon high in the sky)	3×10^{-1}	object recognition
moonlight (full moon)	10^{-1}	
moonlight (half moon)		limit of colour and detail vision
clear starlight (GSR conditions for II sights)	10^{-3}	crude outline perception
overcast starlight/overcast dull	10^{-4}	crude contrast perception
very overcast starlight	10^{-5}	
	10^{-6}	threshold of vision

Colour, then, is another important visual cue to the presence of an object of interest in a daylight scene. Less obviously, however, in consequence of the development of imagers which respond to wavelengths *outside* the visible spectrum, particularly in parts of the infra-red spectrum (from IR-sensitive daylight cameras and image intensifiers to the many available thermal-imaging devices), is the possibility of multi-spectral variations in reflectivity which generate new

15

problems for the art of camouflage (in particular, see Chapter 4, where the use of intensifiers which are sensitive to near IR radiation demands IR-reflecting camouflage).

Other visual cues are the presence of sharp edges, identifiable outlines or differences in 'texture'. All these cues are readily seized on by the eye/brain processing system, which has evolved over time to produce a very powerful recognition system. Quantifying these effects so that they can be measured and used by artificial 'intelligent' systems is an area where there is a considerable amount of research and progress, though current systems fall a long way short of the power and flexibility of the human observer.

Photometry-Optical Units

In the previous section, we used the term 'brightness' because it is a useful, everyday word to describe how light or dark something appears to be. For calculating or specifying the performance of equipment it is necessary to be rather more precise. The scientific term which expresses what we usually describe as an object's brightness is *luminance* (symbol L) which is measured in candelas per square metre (cd/m^2).

In the SI system of units the *candela* (cd) is the unit of light output from a small light source (that is, a source which is so small that the observer views the light as if it all came from a single point, rather than an extended object). The candela is defined in terms of the light output from a specific, reproducible source (a specified small area of solidifying platinum at its melting point). For objects in the everyday scene, which we see because they are emitting or reflecting light over a significant area, our experience of brightness relates to their light output in candelas per unit *apparent* area, as seen from our direction, and is thus measured in candelas per square metre.

The luminance of a particular object will depend on the amount of light falling on it (the ambient illuminance), and also on how much of the incident light it reflects in the observer's direction. This will depend on the nature of the material the object is made of and its surface characteristics. Fortunately, many objects with matt surfaces scatter incoming light in a very particular way, appearing equally bright, almost regardless of the direction of the observer. Such surfaces are known as *Lambertian* surfaces. For such a surface, if it is illuminated by E lux and its reflectivity is r, its resulting luminance, L, is given by

$$L = \frac{r\,E}{\pi} \qquad \text{(in cd per m}^2\text{)}.$$

These quantities and units are known as *photometric* units. It is necessary to use them for optical measurements because they measure things in a manner which corresponds to the way in which they are perceived by the eye, which is not equally sensitive to all wavelengths of visible light, and not sensitive at all to other types of electromagnetic energy. A more detailed account of them, and the parallel system of *radiometric* quantities, is given in Annex A.

LENS SYSTEMS

The first task for any imaging system is to collect light from the objects in the scene and redirect the light rays to form a focused image. This task is usually done by a lens or lens system known as the *objective* lens, though it can also be done by using reflecting optics. The focusing power of a simple lens is usually specified by measuring the distance from the lens to the image of a very distant object. This is known as the focal length, *f*. In ordinary surveillance systems, it is likely to have a value between roughly 50 and a few hundred millimetres. It turns out that the larger the focal length of a lens, the larger the image it produces. Figure 2.3 illustrates this: the ray from the top of the object which passes through the centre of the lens continues in a straight line, so the final image *height* is determined by the distance to the focused image. The sizes of the image and object, h_i and h_o, and the focal length (f) and range (R) are then related by the formula

$$\frac{h_i}{h_o} = \frac{f}{R}$$

Although this formula is based on the theory of simple, thin lenses and distant

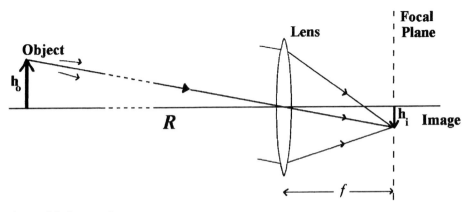

Figure 2.3 Image Geometry

objects, it remains true for more general imaging surveillance systems, where f is now the *effective* focal length of the system.

It is thus the focal length of the lens, together with the physical size of the image area, detector elements, etc, that combine to dictate the range at which an object of a particular size may be distinguished, how large an object must be in order to be visible at a particular range, and the overall field of view of the system. Unfortunately, increasing the focal length also means that the resulting image is fainter and the field of view smaller, other things being equal.

Image Brightness and F-number

As noted above, increasing the focal length of a lens spreads the light in an image out and thus reduces its brightness. If the image brightness is to be maintained, the *useful* diameter of the lens (often known as its *aperture*) needs to be increased in the same proportion. In order to specify how efficient a lens is at collecting enough light to form a useful image, it is usual to specify the *F*-number of the lens (*F#*). This actually represents the ratio of the lens's focal length to its diameter, given by:

$$F\text{–number} = \frac{\text{focal length, } f}{\text{diameter}}$$

Indeed, lens apertures are often specified as '*f*/xx', where xx is the *F*-number of the lens.

For a lens of a given *F*-number and transmission t, an object of luminance L will produce an image whose illuminance, E_I is

$$E_I = \frac{\pi\, t\, L}{4\, (F\#)^2} \quad lux$$

The value given by this expression can be compared with details given in the manufacturers' information on surveillance equipment, such as cameras or image intensifiers, to see whether a particular piece of equipment can carry out a particular requirement, or what type of lens it will need to work under given conditions. For maximum light collection, a large diameter lens is required, resulting in a low value for the *F*-number. In practice, *F*-numbers cannot easily be made much smaller than 1 ('*f*/$_{1.0}$'), and are usually around 1.4 to 3.5 for general purpose systems. Large aperture lenses collect more light, but they are inevitably bulky and difficult (and expensive) to design and manufacture if they are to give a picture of sufficient clarity.

Image Detail and Field of View

In many optical sytems, such as cameras or image intensifiers, the objective lens focuses an image direct on to a sensor material, and the dimensions of the *useful* image area are determined by the working size of this detector. The larger the focal length of the objective lens, the larger the image it will form of a given object. If the area available for the image is restricted by the sensor, this automatically curtails the field of view; indeed, because light rays passing through the centre of the lens continue in a straight line, the angular field of view of the system will be equal to the angle subtended by the detector from the centre of the lens (see Figure 2.4). Thus to a good approximation, the field of view of an image intensifier with a standard 18mm diameter intensifier unit and a 120mm focal length lens is 150 mils, or slightly over 8.5 degrees.

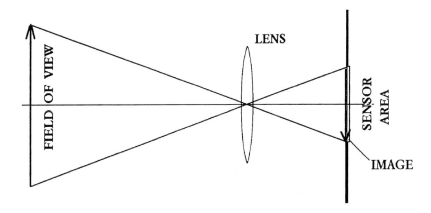

Figure 2.4 Field of View of EO Systems

Within the image area in any system, however good, there will also be a limit to the fineness of the detail which it can portray. For most everyday surveillance systems, this limitation is imposed by the physical structure of the sensor, though lens sytems can and do have performance limitations of their own. For the sensor it will be determined by the size and spacing of the individual sensor elements, or by the precision with which the effects of the incoming light are confined to the point where the light falls. For a lens it is determined by the quality of the focusing over the range of wavelengths concerned and also by the sophistication of the design of the components of the focusing system, particularly for large apertures or extreme fields of view. Ultimately too, any focusing system must also be limited by the wave nature of light itself. This causes the waves of light which should be focused to a single point to spread from their path slightly, resulting in an imperfect focus. This effect is known as *diffraction*, and is a particular problem for high magnification systems for aerial or satellite surveillance, where very long focal length lenses are often required.

The limited ability of any practical system to distinguish detail perfectly is often quantified as a maximum *spatial frequency* that the system can resolve, where the word 'frequency' simply describes how rapidly the image is varying in *space* (rather than time). This is often stated in terms of the maximum number of black and white bar pattern cycles which can just be 'seen' by the device, measured in cycles per millimetre in the image (often described as *line-pairs* per mm), or, for complete systems, such as the eye or weapon sights, as cycles per unit angle of the field of view. An alternative description much used for video cameras and displays is in terms of equivalent TV lines per picture height (that is, the total number of vertical black *and* white lines that it can resolve in a distance equal to the height of the picture). All three of these measures are in common use, depending on the type of system under consideration. These are illustrated in Figure 2.5 where the finer of the two bar charts could be described as having a spatial frequency of 4 cycles per mm, 0.08 cycles per mil (20/250) or 24 TV lines per picture height.

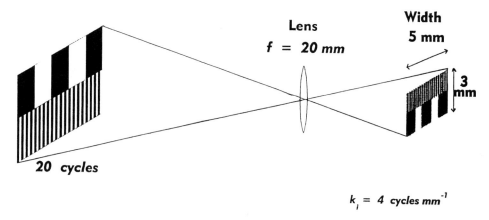

Figure 2.5 Image Spatial Frequency

PERFORMANCE ASSESSMENT

Detection, Recognition and Identification

As we saw in the first chapter, it is useful to distinguish three successive levels of perception in the process of surveillance, from *detection*, when an object can just be discriminated from its background, through *recognition*, when the observer can say what *type* of object it is, to *identification*.

These stages are obviously related to how clearly the object can be seen. This is determined by a number of factors related to the object and to the scene as a whole. Many of them are related to the *visual cues* discussed above, and the presence of background *clutter* is a further complication for the observer; but the most important factor is the capability of the system to portray *detail* in an image at the appropriate level of contrast.

The Johnson Criteria

One useful way of relating the operational value of a particular surveillance device to readily determined test measurements has come to be known as the *Johnson criteria*. Following extensive trials with trained observers, a variety of different imagers and a number of different test objects (ranging from individual soldiers to main battle tanks), the resolution requirements for detection, recognition, etc. were found to be reasonably consistent when related to the minimum dimension of the test object concerned.

The criteria were established as follows: the targets were viewed through an electro-optical sensor and their range changed until the images on the display could only just be detected by 50 per cent of the observers. The real targets were then replaced by a succession of bar charts of 'black and white' stripes of similar contrast to that of the targets and the background to determine the resolution capability of the system at this point. Knowing the angle subtended by the objects and the number of cycles resolvable by the the system per unit angle of the field of view, the number of resolvable cycles per minimum target dimension corresponding to detection could be found. The range of the real target was reduced until it could just be *recognised* by 50 per cent of the observers and the procedure repeated. A similar process was performed for identification.

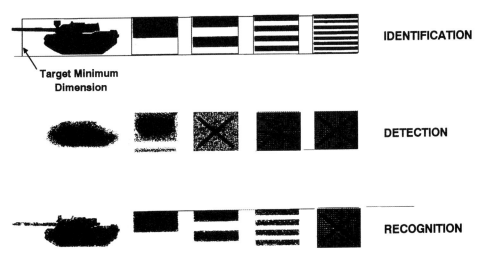

Figure 2.6 The Johnson Criteria

The results showed that for a 50 per cent probability of being correct under a variety of conditions:

a. Detection required a resolution capability of approximately one cycle per minimum target dimension.
b. Recognition required three to five cycles per minimum target dimension.
c. Identification required six to seven cycles per minimum target dimension.

These are illustrated in Figure 2.6. The top line shows the test object, which can be seen reasonably clearly, together with a number of bar charts which are all resolvable. The object can be identified, and the observer can resolve around seven cycles within the height of the tank. The second line shows the situation at *detection*, when the tank is only perceptible to 50 per cent of the observers as an indistinct blob which is distinct from its background. The average resolution capability at this level was just one single light/dark cycle in the angle subtended by the tank, the more detailed bar charts were completely unresolvable.

For *recognition* an intermediate amount of detail is required. On average, allowing for a certain variabiity with different types and orientations of target, recognition required the ability to resolve four cycles in the minimum target dimension.

For specification purposes these figures are often taken as one, four and eight, respectively, but it is best to quote the figure one is using. These criteria enable us to find the performance limits required of a surveillance system if it is to meet a given requirement. Putting the image size in terms of spatial frequency, k_i, and the number of cycles (cy), N, required by the Johnson criteria converts the lens equation we met earlier into a useful relation between operational ranges and system resolution. This is shown in Figure 2.7. It shows, for example, that to identify a target 2m high, at a range of 1 km with a 100mm focal length lens, the system should be capable of recording detail up to a spatial frequency of 40 cy mm^{-1}; if the response extends out to 80 cy mm^{-1}, then theoretically at least it should be capable of identification at 2km.

VISION AND THE EYE

The previous section discussed the performance requirements for a sensor to carry out its role to a given degree of discrimination. We turn now to our own imaging sensor, which is the means by which the available information is relayed to the brain. The eye is an immensely versatile sensor, and one capable of very useful performance under a wide range of conditions. Understanding the effect of the conditions on its performance is a necessary part of understanding and using other surveillance devices intended to enhance its capabilities.

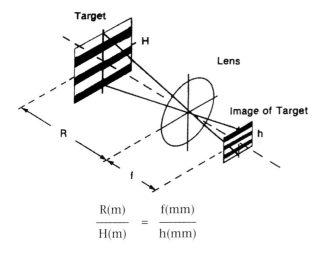

$$\frac{R(m)}{H(m)} = \frac{f(mm)}{h(mm)}$$

Let N = no. of cycles per minimum target dimension

$$\frac{NR}{H} = \frac{Nf}{h} = fk_i$$

where k_i = no. of cycles [cy] per mm on the image

$$\therefore \quad \boxed{k_i = \frac{R}{Hf} \; N}$$

for R = 1000 m
H = 2m
f = 100m $\qquad k_i = \frac{1000}{2 \times 100} \times n = 5N \text{ cy mm}^{-1}$

for Detection   N = 1 k_{iDET} = 5cy mm^{-1}
    Recognition   N = 4 k_{iREC} = 20 cy mm^{-1} when R = 1 km
    Identification N = 8 k_{iIDEN} = 40 cy mm^{-1}

Figure 2.7 System Resolution Requirements

The eye is often thought of as being like a camera and in many ways this is a useful analogy; but it is in fact vastly more complex and versatile than any camera yet devised, both because of the range of conditions it can work under and because of the highly sophisticated way in which it extracts information from the scene and alerts the brain to the most significant aspects of it.

The basic structure of the eye is shown in Figure 2.8. Like the camera, the eye has a controllable focusing system designed to give a sharp image of objects of

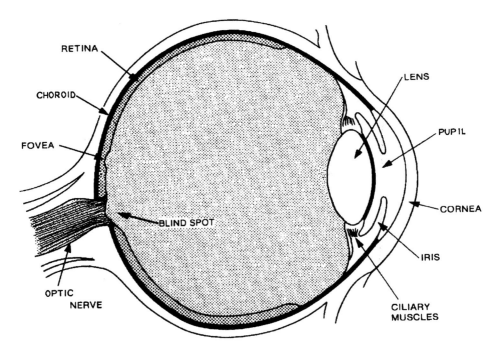

Figure 2.8 Cross-Section of the Human Eye

interest. When relaxed, the average eye has an *effective* focal length of 16.7mm. Close-up objects require a powerful focusing action and the muscles surrounding the lens tighten to squeeze it into a more curved, shorter focal-length, configuration.

Like the camera, the amount of light entering the eye can be controlled to a degree by varying the diameter of the pupil, opening the pupil to a maximum diameter of around 7mm under poor light conditions, or rapidly closing it down to about 2mm under bright lights. This is achieved by adjusting the muscles controlling the iris and is most useful as a quick-acting protective mechanism, protecting the eye against very strong lights, for instance. The eye pupil size also sets important constraints in the design and use of optical systems, as we shall see later.

In a camera the image is focused on to a flat photographic film, uniformly coated with chemicals in a balance which is specially selected for a given range of illumination conditions. In the eye the task of converting the optical image into an electrical signal for transmission to the brain is carried out by the *retina*. This highly sensitive arrangement of cells lines a large proportion of the interior of the eye; it is roughly hemispherical in shape, and consists of a complicated structure of detector cells, nerves and connecting cells. The state of the detector cells is 'sensed' by one or more bipolar connecting cells and these in turn are sensed by nerve endings. Information is then gathered through a network of around a million individual nerves and assembled into the *optic nerve* (see Figure 2.9), which is led out from the interior of the eye at the so-called 'blind spot'.

The highly complex nature of these interconnections is responsible for many of the practical aspects of vision that we shall comment on later. Immediately behind the retina lies the *choroid*, which is a special, very dark layer carrying a blood supply rich in the nutrients necessary for detector cell operation, such as vitamin A. This has the additional advantage of absorbing light which has passed straight through the rest of the retina, so that it is not scattered around, detracting from the contrast in the focused image.

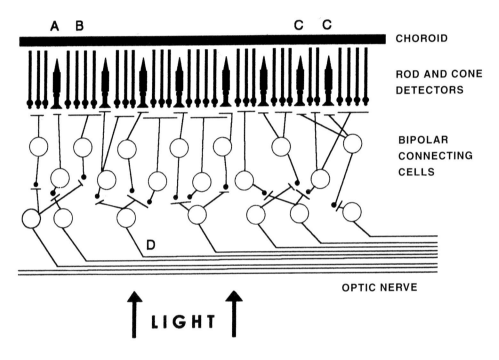

A: *One cone cell connected to an individual nerve.*

B: *Cluster of rod cells connected to one nerve.*

C: *Several cones connected to one nerve.*

D: *Complex groups of cells connected to one nerve.*

Figure 2.9 Structure of the Retina

Detailed examination of the retina reveals two quite distinct types of receptor cell, known as *rod* and *cone* cells, because of their appearance (the cone cells having a tapered section at the end). Although present in small numbers over almost all of the retina, the cone cells are particularly highly concentrated in a relatively small area right in the centre of the field of view, known as the *fovea*. For most of the area of the retina, the rod cells dominate, numbering around 120 million, as opposed to only 6.8 million cone cells. Being at the centre of our field of view, it is on the fovea that we focus the light from objects at which we are looking directly, and the large number of cone cells here are responsible for the clarity with which we see things over a relatively small central field of view. Many of the cone cells here are connected either individually or in small numbers to individual nerves (see letters A and C in Figure 2.9). The cones are so densely packed in the very central area that they are squashed into a fraction of the space they usually occupy and rod cells are completely excluded.

The distribution of these two types of cell has important consequences for the way we see things both by day and by night and is shown in Figure 2.10. The role of both types of detector cell is to convert incoming light into an electrical signal, and the fundamental operation of the two types of cell is similar, though there are also some important differences between them. Both sets of cells contain photochemical pigments (dyes) whose molecules are changed (temporarily) on exposure to light. This chemical change produces a change in the electrical potential at the 'connector' end of the cell, which may trigger the intermediate layer of cells (the 'bipolar' connecting cells) to stimulate an appropriate nerve.

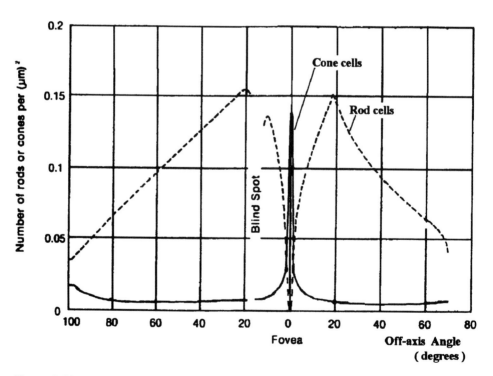

Figure 2.10 Distribution of Rod and Cone Cells in the Retina

The pigment in the rod cells is rhodopsin. It bleaches rapidly on exposure to light and is thus highly sensitive. A similar process takes place in the cone cells, which are now known to contain three different, closely related pigments (iodopsins). These are considerably less sensitive to light than rhodopsin, demanding significantly higher light levels to work effectively. The cone cells also differ from rod cells in that the three distinct pigments respond to different bands of wavelengths in the visible spectrum. This has the result that the signal sent to the brain from combinations of cone cells (such as at C in Figure 2.9) conveys the sensation of colour. In effect, the interconnecting cells are sensing and comparing the output of several cone cells to generate colour information.

It is clear from this that the cone cells and the rod cells correspond to two quite distinct visual systems, which we may regard as operating by day and by night, respectively, though they share many of the same nerves and connector cells. Under good lighting conditions, the cone cells which are highly concentrated in the fovea give us highly detailed colour vision, the rod cells are effectively dazzled (the rhodopsin is bleached) and so they contribute no information. By night (by starlight and below), there is not enough light for the cone cells to provide useful information (though, of course, if more light is suddenly available, they will contribute), but the rod cells provide us with monochrome, low-resolution information. This may be related to the progressive loss of vision capability seen in Table 2.1. In order to distinguish between the two different 'seeing' mechanisms, they are often known as *photopic* and *scotopic* vision (from the Greek for 'light' and 'dark').

The relative response curves for the rod and cone cells are shown in Figure 2.11. The difference between the two curves give rise to several practical consequences. First, the cone cell (daylight) curve has its maximum value almost exactly at the wavelength of the peak output of the sun. The rod cells have a somewhat shorter peak wavelength owing to the fact that light at these wavelengths is more energetic and thus more likely to be detected (see the discussion of *photons* in Chapter 3). This gives rise to an apparent change in the relative brightness of different coloured objects as light levels fall, while both detector mechanisms are operational. Blue objects appear relatively brighter than before and red objects, such as pillar boxes, appear darker. This is known as the Purkinje effect, and from the practical point of view it is one of the factors which makes familiar objects look unfamiliar, causing some sense of disorientation.

A further contributory factor is that without colour information shadow areas are more difficult to distinguish from real objects. Note that in order to get the two curves on to one graph, the sensitivity axis uses logarithmic spacing. Interestingly, this reveals the eye's real, but very low sensitivity to extreme wavelengths. A linear plot of the cone cell response is given in Figure A1 (in the Annex to this chapter), appearing to show no response to wavelengths above

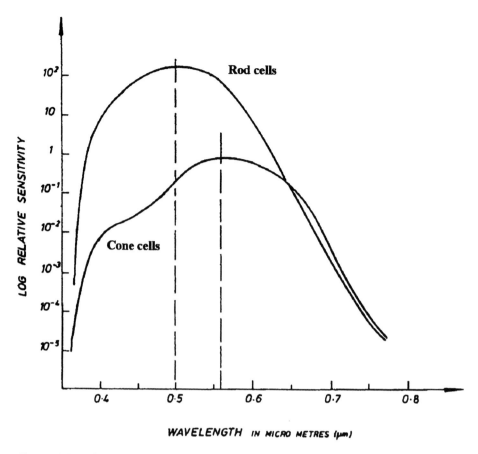

Figure 2.11 The Spectral Response of the Eye

0.7µm, or below 0.4µm. In fact, the eye does have a capability slightly beyond these wavelengths, though examination of the scale in Figure 2.11 shows that this is *extremely* weak. Nevertheless, it can be sufficient to call the observer's attention to supposedly covert light sources, including some 'IR' LEDs and active IR sources.

Dark Adaptation

As we have seen above, because of the much greater sensitivity of the rod cells to most visible wavelengths, under daylight conditions the rhodopsin is effectively bleached out. The regeneration process is slow, so that on sudden exposure to poor lighting conditions it takes a substantial period of time for the rhodopsin levels to build up to their optimum value. This process is known as 'dark adaptation' and is a familiar experience in everyday life.

Figure 2.12 shows how the ability of the eye to detect faint light sources

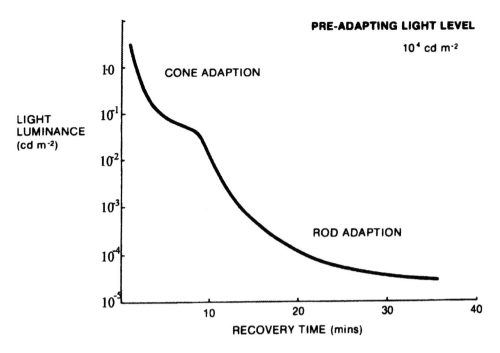

Figure 2.12 Variation of Sensitivity with Time (Dark Adaptation)

improves with time in darkness (shown on a logarithmic scale). Initially there is a relatively quick but modest improvement due to pigment build-up in the cone cells. This is then followed by the much more protracted improvement in sensitivity, over several orders of magnitude, as the rhodopsin in the rod cells builds up to maximum concentration after half an hour or more.

In order to be able to preserve this highly extended capability and operate effectively under low-light conditions, it is imperative to maintain one's state of dark adaptation by protecting the eyes from extended exposure to bright lights. To this end, it is interesting to note that, as may be seen from the response curves of Figure 2.12, the rod cells are no more sensitive to red light than the cone cells (and in the extreme red, rather less sensitive). Imaging devices and displays using low-level red light can thus be used (arguably), viewed by the cone cells without serious detriment to night vision. A variety of equipments intended for occasional use at night capitalise on this, ranging from portable thermal imaging sights to LED information displays.

VISUAL RESOLUTION

Because the eye uses a large array of individual sensors to convert a focused image into nerve impulses and conveys the information along an even more limited number of nerves, there is inevitably a limit to the fineness of objects or features in an image which can be discriminated from one another. On a large scale, as we have seen, the distribution of the cone cells is highly varied. This results in a 'general purpose' field-of-view of around 40° horizontally and 30° in elevation, which is reflected in the 4 × 3 aspect ratio of conventional TV and the rectangular format of most imaging systems.

Within this general field of view, the fovea provides high quality imagery across about 9° at the centre and 'best' vision is limited to around a degree in diameter. Normally, however, we are unaware of this variability of detail, partly because the eye is continually and involuntarily scanning the scene to update our mental image of what is there.

The ability of the eye to detect fine detail can be measured in a variety of ways, but for our purposes it is most usefully found using a series of black and white (100 per cent contrast) bar-charts where the bar width is related to the bar spacing. The spacing of the finest bars which can be distinguished is recorded and this measurement is converted into an angular measurement in order to allow comparison and prediction for different ranges. Visual resolution, or 'visual acuity', is thus measured here in terms of the number of cycles which the eye can discern per unit angle. Under good illumination conditions the eye can detect bar charts with around 2.7 cycles per milliradian (on the visual axis), i.e., 2.7 cycles per millimetre at 1 metre. Off axis, visual activity is found to fall off rapidly, effectively following the cone cell spacing of Figure 2.10.

Investigation of the variation of resolution with the brightness, or luminance, of the bar charts gives rise to the curve shown in Figure 2.13. Under good lighting conditions, the resolution of the eye remains reasonably constant, but this deteriorates rapidly under twilight conditions and below. Note how the rod cells come into operation at lower light levels, but with a greatly reduced capability to discriminate detail. This occurs because the rod cells are always connected through to the optic nerve in clusters which vary in size up to several thousands (unlike the cone cells, as we have seen above). This is shown at letter B in figure 2.9.

By night, the rod cell acuity varies in a quite different way from that for the cone cells, even allowing for their much poorer resolution. Because of the relative absence of rod cells from the fovea, we see things very badly when looking straight at them; rod cell vision is at its best around 10° to 15° off the visual axis, corresponding to the rather curious experience of seeing things best under poor light conditions when looking somewhat away from them. The variation of rod cell acuity across the field of view is similar in outline to the rod-cell-curve in Figure 2.10, though the peak is rather closer to the visual axis as the nerve connections also vary.

We referred earlier to the complexity of the interconnections, and we have seen how unlike a simple photographic camera the detailed structure of the eye is, providing us with alternate sensing sytems, colour information by day and

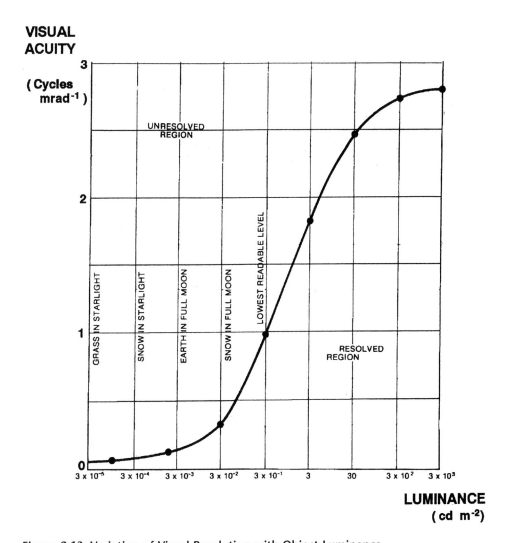

Figure 2.13 Variation of Visual Resolution with Object Luminance

variable resolution across the field of view. One further aspect of this complexity is worth mentioning as it too relates to the all-important ability to pick out objects in our field of view. Although we have looked at several relatively simple routes by which the information from the detectors is transmitted to the brain, the retina actually contains many far more convoluted connections. Some cone cells, particularly at the periphery of the field of view, are connected in a way which sends the brain information about rapid changes in intensity, presumably to alert us to moving objects well away from the centre of the field of view, and as a result, the eye is particularly responsible to flicker in the scene. In addition to its evolutionary advantages, this places some constraints and poses some problems for the design of electro-optic displays.

Research has shown that many of the nerves to the brain carry information about edges in the field of view, by comparing the outputs of multiple groups of cone and rod cells (such as at letter D in Figure 2.9). Different nerves respond to edges in different directions, so in addition to straightforward image information, the brain is also receiving direct information about outlines and patterns, giving the observer his important ability to recognise objects and assess situations rapidly.

Visual Resolution and Contrast

Visual activity measurements are intended to assess the ultimate discrimination of the eye and thus use patterns such as bar charts with strong contrast. Real life scenery often consists of much smaller degrees of contrast and more complex (and less well-defined) objects. A wide variety of measurements of visual resolution at lower degrees of contrast have been undertaken. These all indicate a reduced ability to see detail as contrast is reduced from black and white, though widely varying results have been found for the lowest contrast at which an image is visible at all.

As we saw, contrast may be defined in several ways, but for visual purposes it is usually defined as the difference of luminance between an object and its background, expressed as a fraction of the background luminance.

$$\text{VISUAL CONTRAST} = \frac{\text{target luminance} - \text{background luminance}}{\text{background luminance}}$$

When both target and background are seen purely by their reflection of the same ambient light, this definition of contrast then reduces to the difference of reflectivities as a fraction of the background reflectivity:

$$C = \frac{r_t - r_b}{r_b}$$

where r_t and r_b are the reflection coefficients of target and background respectively.

For large, static objects, such as a landscape viewed against a skyline, it is usual to take the threshold of visibility as a 2 per cent contrast, using the above definition. Smaller distant objects will generally not be apparent until a contrast of 5 per cent is achieved. The required level of contrast for detection purposes has been found to depend on the size and distance of the targets used (i.e., on the angle subtended at the observer). Most measurements have concentrated on the ability of observers to discern low-contrast rectangular or smoothly varying bar charts, which are inherently repetitive, and the eye is capable of detecting the regularity of low-contrast patterns at much lower levels than are needed for small, distant objects. Given an extended bar pattern with a suitable spatial frequency the eye can detect variations with a contrast as small as 0.5 per cent or less.

For our purposes, where we wish to connect the resolving capability of an observer to his ability to carry out detection and recognition of distant, low-contrast targets, the most useful measurements use bar charts which are a relatively small part of the field of view and thus require a reasonable level of contrast for detection. Results of such tests provide resolving capabilities varying as shown in Figure 2.14, which is based on reasonably good daytime illumination.

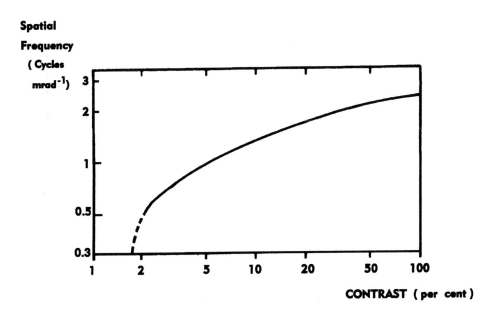

Figure 2.14 Visual Resolution and Contrast

ATMOSPHERIC TRANSMISSION, CONTRAST AND VISIBILITY

Light travelling from the scene to the observer has passed through the intervening atmospheric constituents and will inevitably be affeted by them to some degree. In addition to the obvious gases, oxygen and nitrogen, which have little effect on the passage of light, the atmosphere contains variable quantities of water vapour, carbon dioxide and ozone. These have an important effect on thermal radiation (and ultra-violet), but only a small effect on visible light.

Apart from gases and vapours, the atmosphere also carries a highly variable population of airborne solid particles and liquid droplets known collectively as aerosols. These are always present to some degree; they cover an enormous range of sizes from small clusters of molecules through mist and smoke particles to substantial raindrops or hailstones (Figure 2.15). All but the largest of these aerosols can be held suspended in the air virtually indefinitely by the motion of the air molecules and currents. The nature and size distribution ranges of the aerosol population vary markedly with location, weather and altitude, but typical constituents are: dust from soil, rock and volcanic debris, ash from forest fires (or clearance), sea-salt crystals and industrial and motor pollutants. Particles are also formed by natural or industrial pollutants condensing out or reacting chemically. Many of these particles are water-soluble and act as condensation centres for water vapour at relative humidities above 35 per cent, giving rise to a constantly changing distribution of particle sizes and water droplets.

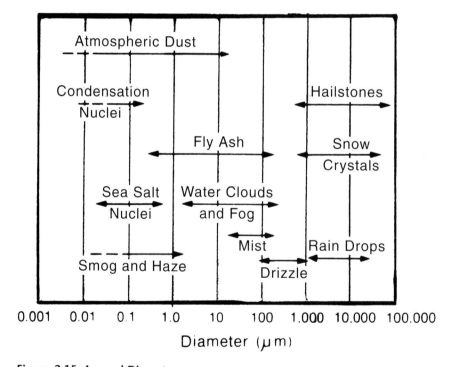

Figure 2.15 Aerosol Diameters

In general, the passage of light may be affected in two ways by the medium it is passing through. First it may be absorbed to some degree. This effect is usually insignificant in the everyday atmospheric transmission of visible light, though it is the dominant effect in thick black smoke etc. The second mechanism is usually much more important for visible light and is known as 'scattering'. This involves light 'bouncing off' either atmospheric molecules or airborne particles (or droplets) and emerging in a different direction (see Figure 2.16). Both these mechanisms cause the amount of light reaching an observer direct from the source to be attenuated, resulting in a gradual (exponential) reduction of directly transmitted light with distance, the rate of attenuation being determined by the prevailing conditions.

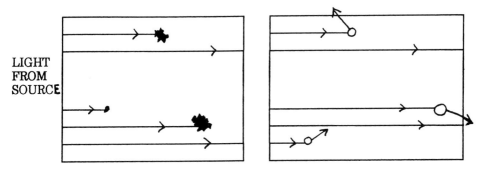

LIGHT
FROM
SOURCE

Figure 2.16 Absorption and Scattering of Light by Aerosols

Mathematically, transmitted light intensity (at range x km), $I_x = I_0 \exp(-\sigma x)$, where σ is the attenuation or 'extinction' coefficient, determined by the several atmospheric constituents. The value of the extinction coefficient, σ, depends strongly on the density and size distribution of the aerosol population. From the point of view of light scattering, it is useful to divide aerosol particles into three size ranges, relative to the wavelength of the scattered radiation:

Particles much smaller than the wavelength (D <λ/10). This is known as 'Rayleigh scattering'. Very small particles individually scatter little light and thus have relatively low extinction coefficient values (low σ). If present in large numbers, and therefore producing a significant degree of scattering, Rayleigh scatterers produce a distinctive extinction coefficient (σ) which varies rapidly with wavelength (σ is proportional to $1/\lambda^4$), so they scatter blue light (short λ) much more than red light (longer λ) resulting in the blue hazy appearance of tobacco smoke, distant mountains on a clear day, and the blue sky itself.

Figure 2.17 shows the contribution of water droplets of a wide range of sizes to atmospheric scattering for light of wavelength 0.55µm. Up to a diameter of 0.05µm the graph rises steeply and steadily, starting from negligibly small values and beginning to deviate from the general trend at the top end of this range. Note that this graph refers to one single particle per cm^3. In reality, Rayleigh scatterers from air and water molecules upwards are present in large numbers, but still do not greatly affect the passage of light at battlefield ranges, unless air turbulence actually distorts the path of the light rays (this may be a real problem for high magnification systems, particularly over long path lengths over absorbing surfaces which have been heated by the sun).

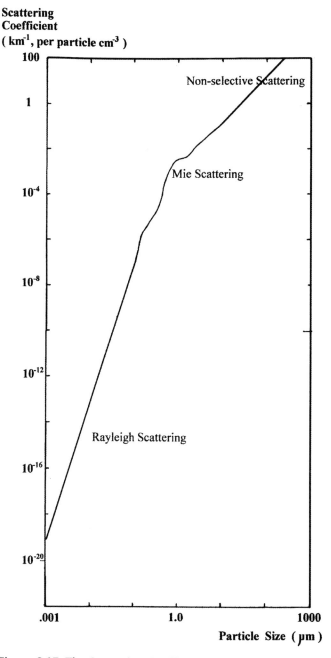

Figure 2.17 The Scattering Coefficient as a Function of Particle Size (for Water Droplets in 0.55μm Visible Light)

Particles of size comparable to the wavelength (D between λ/10 and 10λ). Particles whose size is comparable to the wavelength are known as 'Mie scatterers'. They scatter light more effectively than Rayleigh scatterers because their physical size can 'resonate' with some possible wave frequencies, giving rise to much higher values for the extiction coefficient as the energy is reradiated. This accounts for the odd shape of Figure 2.17 in this region, as the curve bends upwards and goes through a series of maxima and minima, depending on the exact relationship between the particle size and the wavelength. Visible light has wavelengths of the order of half a micrometer, and particles of this size range are generated in large numbers by a variety of means, such as mist, pollution and heavy smoke. Mie scattering is thus a particular problem for visible light surveillance as particles of this size range can remain airborne for long periods of time.

Table 2.2   Contributions to Atmospheric Attenuation

Conditions	Air Molecules		Aerosol		Overall attenuation coefficient σ [km^{-1}]	5km transmission	Visual Range (Met) [km]
	Abs'n	Scat	Abs'n	Scat.			
exc. clear	0	.01	.005	0.025	0.04	82%	98.5
clear	0	.01	.020	0.19	0.22	33%	18
hazy (light haze)	0	.01	.050	0.94	1.0	0.7%	3.9
mist	0	.01	.100	20	20.1	–	0.2

Particles much larger than the wavelength (D >10λ). Much larger particles, such as fog droplets or rain, scatter light by redirecting it in random directions. The degree of scattering depends purely on the particle cross-sectional area. It does not vary with wavelength, but only on their concentration. This is known as 'non-selective' scattering. It is exhibited by clouds, fog, rain and hailstorms for visible light, and has a white or grey appearance. Concentrations of such particles may be very high in clouds or fog, giving rise to values of σ of well over 100 km^{-1}.

In general, longer wavelengths lead to better transmission, hence the use of coloured filters in some binoculars and improved visibility in image intensifiers sensitive to near IR. Furthermore, aerosol particles which are Mie scatterers limiting *visible* range act as Rayleigh scatterers for TI or radar, which can thus see more clearly through smoke or haze. In the same way, fog droplets act as Mie scatterers for TI and are penetrated only by radar wavelengths.

EFFECT OF SCATTERING ON CONTRAST

Scattering reduces the amount of light reaching the observer direct from the source *and* the background. At the same time as this light is scattered *out* of the path, light from elsewhere (the sky, other background, etc.) is scattered *into* the path and is superimposed on the light from the target. This results in a 'washing out' of the light and dark of the scene, tending to reduce it to a uniform grey. Scattering thus reduces the contrast between the object and the background by mixing in stray light from elsewhere (see Figure 2.18).

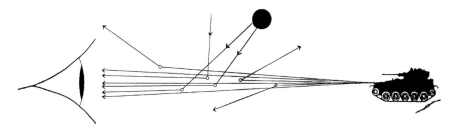

Figure 2.18 Contrast Loss due to Light Scattering

To a reasonable approximation, contrast is found to fall off exponentially with range, at a rate governed by the attenuation coefficient, σ.

$$C_R = C_0 \exp(-\sigma R).$$

See Figure 2.19

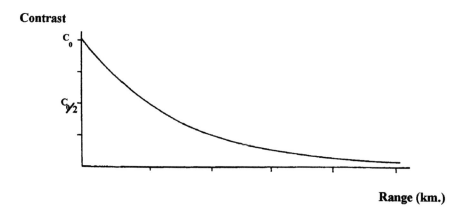

Figure 2.19 Exponential Contrast Loss with Range

Visual range

The limit of visibility set by meteorologists is defined as the range at which a 100 per cent contrast is reduced to 2 per cent, rendering the distinction between the object and its background barely perceptible.

Then $C_M = .02C_0$,

giving $0.02 = \exp(-\sigma R_M)$, or $R_M = -\log(0.02)/\sigma$;

i.e., meteorological visual range = $3.9/\sigma$.

In very foggy conditions, σ may be as high as 120km^{-1} or even more, giving a (meteorological) visual range of about 30m.

For military purposes, where it is important to be able to see smaller, mobile objects, a threshold contrast of 5 per cent has been accepted as more realistic. The same calculation then gives a *useful* military visual range:

$$R_{MIL.VIS} = 3.0/\sigma,$$

though low contrast targets will cease to be visible well within this distance.

ANNEXE

Practical Optical Units

The main text of Chapter 2 concentrated on the optical units which are necessary to understand and quantify system performance. A fuller explanation of these units and the way that they relate to each other is often necessary for the more detailed calculations involved in specifying system requirements.

For optical measurements, the central idea is the 'amount of light flow', or luminous flux, F. This is in effect a measure of the amount of energy flow, but weighted to allow for the fact that different wavelengths (i.e., colours) do not produce the same degree of sensation in the eye.

The unit of luminous flux is the lumen (lm), and, at the peak sensitivity of daylight vision (555 nm), 1 watt of light energy is equivalent to 680 lumens. At other wavelengths, the quantity of luminous flux corresponding to 1 watt of energy flow is reduced in proportion to the sensitivity of the eye at that wavelength, V_λ (see Figure A1). For a given wavelength:

$$\text{luminous flux, } F_\lambda = \text{energy flow} \times 680\ V_\lambda.$$

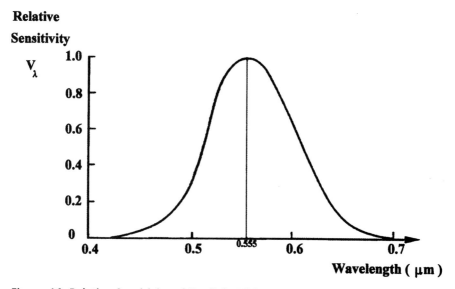

Figure A1 Relative Sensitivity of Daylight Vision

A lamp producing 1 watt of 555 nm green/yellow light will appear much brighter than a lamp producing 1 watt of blue or red light, and a source producing ultraviolet or infra-red radiation does not produce any *visible* flux at all, however great the energy flow. The 'luminous efficacy' of a light source describes the conversion efficiency of turning electrical power (in watts) into useful light (in lumens). For filament lights, this is very low, typically only 10 to 20 lm W^{-1}. Fluorescent lamps are somewhat better (around 70 lm W^{-1}).

For example: A mercury lamp emits light of wavelengths 0.58, 0.55, 0.435, 0.405 and 0.36µm, with energy outputs of 0.5, 0.7, 0.9, 0.6, and 1.0 watts, respectively. What is the total luminous flux emitted by the lamp? If the total power input is 16 W, what is its luminous efficacy?

From the graph we can determine the V_λ values at each wavelength, and multiplying each by the appropriate power output gives the luminous flux for each wavelengeh. Adding together each of the contributions,

total flux = 762 lm, giving a luminous efficacy of 47.6 lm W^{-1}

Further photometric quantities

For practical measurements, three further photometric quantities are useful:

Illuminance. Illuminance, E, is the total quantity of light falling on a surface; it is the degree of illumination and is the density of light arriving on the surface in lumens per square metre (see Figure A2). This enables us to measure local conditions or to specify a standard for equipment requirements. Because of its importance, illuminance has its own unit, the lux (= 1 lm m^{-2}).

Average Illuminance,

E = F/A lux

Figure A2 Illuminance

Luminous intensity. Luminous intensity, I, describes the intensity of a point source of light. One could in principle specify a light source purely by the total amount of luminous flux it generated, but no practical source sends the same quantity of flux in all directions. Luminous intensity solves this problem by specifying how much flux has been emitted into a given sector of space or solid angle (see Figure A3).

Figure A3 Luminous Intensity

Its unit is the *candela* (cd), which is the SI base unit for photometric measurements, the other optical units are defined in terms of it. 1 candela is $\frac{1}{60}$ of the luminous intensity of a 1cm^2 area of a black-body at the temperature of solidifying platinum. The amount of energy being produced can be calculated separately, and from the spectral sensitivity of the eye and the spectral distribution of the radiation, we arrive at the equivalence of 1 watt to 680 lm of 555 nm light given earlier.

Luminous intensity thus measures the density of flux in lumens per steradian of space radiating out from the source in the direction of interest. For a perfect, isotropic source, its luminous intensity I is given by $F/4\pi$, though practical sources will depart from this formula by different amounts in different directions. Luminous intensity is a useful way of describing small light sources such as filament bulbs in which the actual source of the light occupies a negligible part of the observer's field of view. A typical 100 watt mains lamp bulb has a luminous intensity of 120 cd. Its light output would therefore be around 1,500 lm if it appeared as bright as this from all directions. This would indicate a luminous efficacy of just 15 lm W^{-1}, due in large part to its invisible IR output and convected heat loss.

For surveillance purposes, we need a way of measuring the brightness of extended objects with a detectable area. The brightness of extended objects is known as their *luminance* (symbol L), whose unit is candelas per m^2 (sometimes called *nits*).

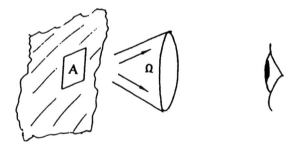

Figure A4 Luminance

Luminance is an appropriate measure both for large light sources close up (e.g., fluorescent tubes) and also for real-world objects which are visible solely because they reflect light. A series of typical values are shown in Table A1. Note that the area concerned is that of the *apparent* area in the observer's field of view, not necessarily the actual area of the object's surface, which may well be at an angle and not flat. This is illustrated in Figure A5.

Many real surfaces appear to have the same brightness from a wide range of angles. This demands that the actual amount of light energy being reflected in

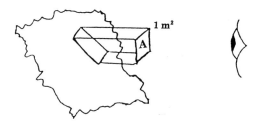

Figure A5 Luminance of Angled Surfaces

different directions follows a specific mathematical distribution, falling off as the area projecting light into the area of the observer's field of view goes up (to be precise, it varies with the cosine of the angle to the right angle with the surface). This is so useful that surfaces following this law are known as *Lambertian* surfaces. For a Lambertian reflecting surface with a reflectivity r and illuminated by E lux it can be shown that:

object luminance, $L = r\, E/\pi$ (in cd m^{-2}, with appropriate units for E).

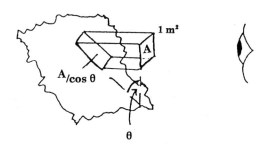

Figure A6 Luminance and Observation Direction

This system of units is useful wherever it is necessary to quantify visible light, either directly for an observer, or for systems whose primary aim is to generate images from purely visible light. Other wavelengths of the electro-magnetic spectrum may also be used for imagery, such as thermal radiation or the near infra-red. These will 'see' the scene in a different way from purely visual systems; quantifying the energy they receive thus requires a different, parallel set of units based on the same concepts as the photometric units outlined above, but based on simple energy quantities, rather than the lumen. These additional quantities are known as *radiometric units*, and are set out in Table A2 below, together with their corresponding photometric units.

43

Table A1   Approximate Luminance Levels of Sources/Surfaces in Candelas per Square Metre

Object	cd m^{-2}
nuclear fireball	5×10^9
upper limit of visual tolerance	10^5
new snow on clear day or upper surface of clouds at noon	3×10^4
$\left(\begin{array}{l}\text{average earth on clear day}\\\text{highlights of a TV screen}\end{array}\right)$	3×10^3
average earth on cloudy day	3×10^2
white page in good reading light	8×10^1
white paper 1 foot from ordinary candle	3
$\left(\begin{array}{l}\text{average page at lowest readable level}\\\text{dark regions of a TV screen}\end{array}\right)$	3×10^{-1}
snow in full moon	2×10^{-2}
ploughland	2×10^{-3}
snow in starlight	2×10^{-4}
green grass in starlight	2×10^{-5}
absolute threshold of seeing	2×10^{-6}

Table A2   Photometric and Radiometric Quantities

Physical Quantity			Psychophysical Quantity		
radiant flux	(P)	W	luminous flux	(F)	lumen (1m)
radiance	(N)	W m^{-2} sr^{-1}	luminance	(L)	lm m^{-2} sr^{-1} cd m^{-2}
radiant exitance (emittance)	(W)	W m^{-2}	luminous exitance	(M)	lm m^{-2}
irradiance	(H)	W m^{-2}	illuminance	(E)	lm m^{-2} (lux)
radiant intensity (watts per unit solid angle)	(J)	W sr^{-1}	luminous intensity	(I)	lm sr^{-1} (candela, cd)

3

Optical and Electro-Optic Systems

INTRODUCTION

Having examined the fundamental elements of imaging surveillance in the previous chapter, we look in this chapter at the variety of aids to our own vision system which play a major role in the vital military task of seeing what is 'out there'. These range from purely conventional optical viewing systems, such as binoculars and daylight weapon sights, through to the rapidly developing range of electro-optic camera systems which make it possible to obtain imagery from situations which are too exposed or physically inaccessible for the observer himself.

OPTICS: SIGHTS, TELESCOPES AND BINOCULARS

Conventional optical surveillance aids have been available to the military observer for a long time, and as such have undergone a steady evolution from the simple telescope to the excellent viewing aids and sights available today. The basic principle of the conventional telescope lies at the heart of all these aids: an objective lens to focus the light from distant objects and an eyepiece which converts this image into a picture which can be scrutinised in detail by the observer.

As ever, the physical size of the first image, and its position, depend on the focal length of the objective lens, f_0. The sytem magnification thus depends on this focal length, but also on the extent of the apparent magnification produced by the eyepiece. This is the design of the conventional astronomical telescope, whose apparent magnification is given by the ratio of the two focal lengths, f_0/f_{eye} (where f_{eye} is the effective focal length of the eyepiece). Two problems arise at once, which make this sytem more appropriate to astronomers than terrestrial observers. First, the image it produces is upside down (because the first focused image is necessarily inverted, and the eyepiece acts as a simple magnifying glass, which does not change the orientation of the resulting image). Secondly, practical magnifications result in devices that are bulky.

Both of these limitations are addressed in conventional binoculars, where the lens configuration is exactly the same, but which use a pair of reflecting prisms to invert the final image and also increase the total light path without adding to the length of the instrument. This is illustrated in Figure 3.1, where the fundamental elements of the design of any optical viewing system may be seen, including the positioning of the graticule. This has to be placed so that it, or its image, coincides with the image formed by the objective (i.e., in the 'focal plane') in order to superimpose calibration marks or a weapon sight on the field of view. Many binoculars intended for military use include a graticule with a scale marked in *mils* of the field of view, enabling the observer to assess the size of objects at a known range or *vice versa*.

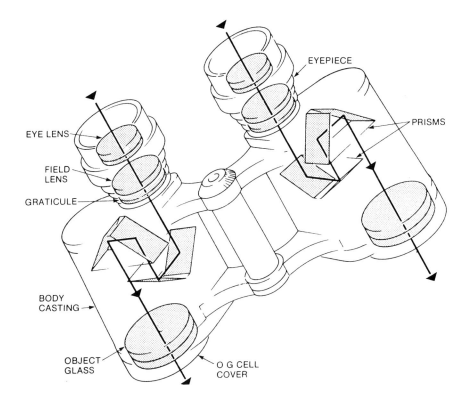

Figure 3.1 Conventional Binocular Design

An alternative way of inverting the image would be to insert an inverting lens, as in a terrestrial telescope. Conventional rifle sights have usually adopted this strategy in order to retain a slim profile, despite the fact that the extra lens adds length and complexity to the instrument without necessarily improving its power; it also introduces a further compromise to the final image quality. Recently a number of sight and binocular designs have used a different prism arrangement, the 'roof prism', to invert the image with an 'inline' design, slimming down the profile of the resulting system. See Figure 3.2. This provides useful, practical weapon sights for modern assault rifles, such as the SUSAT sight.

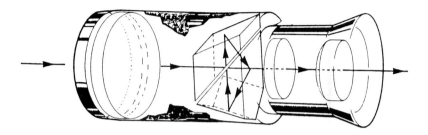

Figure 3.2 'Roof Prism' Optics

Practical System Parameters

A number of parameters and design constraints are important for any optical system. Clearly the magnification and field of view are important considerations, determined partly by the role of the system, but also by practical considerations. Magnification, for instance, is a desirable feature of systems intended to help one see distant objects, but as we have noted, it is obtained at the expense of field of view. It also has the effect of magnifying instrument motion, so unsupported, hand-held binoculars become difficult to see through clearly at magnifications above × 10 owing to natural hand tremor.

Magnification has a further drawback as we saw in the section on f-numbers, the larger the image generated with a given amount of light, the fainter it becomes. It is possible to collect more light by increasing the diameter of the objective lens, but this does not automatically improve the brightness of the image generated in the observer's eye because light entering the eye is restricted by the physical size of the pupil.

It turns out that increasing the objective diameter also increases the area over which light emerges from the instrument and may well make it larger than the eye pupil, in which case the extra light is wasted. Fortunately, this effect is simply quantified. The area filled by light emerging from binoculars or a telescope can actually be seen if it is held up towards a lighted area but held away from the eye. It appears as a bright circular image in the region just outside the eyepiece. This is known as the *exit pupil* (see Figure 3.3), and for these systems its size is given by:

$$\text{Exit pupil diameter} = \frac{\text{Objective diameter}}{\text{Magnification}}$$

Figure 3.3 The Exit Pupil

Exit pupils slightly larger than the eye pupil are not necessarily bad if the system is to be used on the move, since it reduces the chances of the eye and the optics becoming misaligned and disturbing the picture being viewed. An exit pupil smaller than the eye's pupil, however, will have the effect of restricting the light entering the eye, which will in turn result in a fainter image of the scene being viewed. Under poor light conditions this will render the system unusable. It is clear from the above that the modestly priced, high magnification, small objective binoculars which look so attractive on the civilian market are of only limited usefulness, being restricted to bright lighting and stable supports even where the image quality is sufficient to justify the magnification.

One further consideration is important for systems liable to motion, whether vehicle sights or weapon sights, and that is the position of the exit pupil. Light leaving the instrument diverges from the exit pupil; it therefore represents the optimum position for the observer's eye to be positioned. The distance between the back of the optics and the exit pupil is known as *eye relief*, and in places where the optics are liable to forceful motion it is desirable to make the eye relief as large as possible so as to avoid painful injuries to the user (Figure 3.4).

Quality Considerations

In addition to the obvious requirement for good quality optics discussed in the previous chapter, there are a variety of other important practical considerations which impinge on the usefulness and the price of a particular piece of

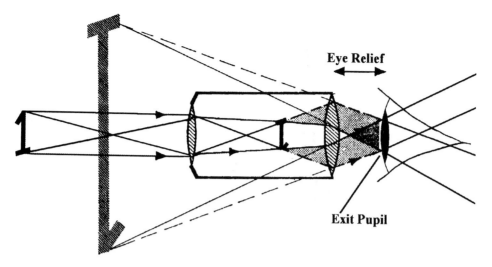

Figure 3.4 Exit Pupil and Eye Relief

equipment. Clearly it is important for any optical system intended for military use that the construction is as robust as possible, consistent with a practical weight, so as to maintain optical and mechanical alignment despite being subjected to mechanical shock. In addition to sheer weight, a further important consideration is balance, so that the equipment may easily be used with confidence. For long-term reliability it is also important that the device should be efficiently sealed to keep out moisture permanently, even in a system with moving parts.

One further important consideration is the optical transmission of the device. Every surface where light travels from one material to another will also result in reflection losses. In an untreated system this may result in half the incoming light being lost. This poses two problems. First, the resulting final image is fainter, limiting the usefulness of the equipment. Even more seriously, the reflected 'lost' light is scattered round the interior of the device, and seen as a veiling 'haze' over the wanted final image, reducing its contrast and clarity. Modern optical systems therefore incorporate anti-reflection coatings on all the optical surfaces, resulting in optical transmission figures of around 90 per cent and good quality, crisp imagery.

ELECTRO-OPTICS: FUNDAMENTALS

In this section we shall look at a variety of ways of converting imagery into an electrical signal which can be viewed remotely. The observer may be in the interior of the vehicle where the imagery is being generated or he may be at some remote station which the images can be relayed to for safety or intelligence purposes. Indeed, the imagery may now be displayed on a number of different monitors, perhaps in different locations, allowing a number of people access to the information generated. Before examining individual devices for carrying this out, however, it is necessary to look in detail at the processes by which light affects materials, and which may thus be capitalised on to produce an imaging system.

Detecting Electromagnetic Energy: Photons

Whenever light or radiation in similar parts of the electromagnetic spectrum interacts with materials, as it must do in a detection system, it becomes apparent that it is fundamentally *quantized* in nature. That is to say, the energy in EM radiation at optical wavelengths and beyond is not transmitted as smooth, continuous waves, but in individual bursts of wave energy known as *photons*. We may picture a photon as a localised burst of wave energy, sharing the characteristic wavelength of the radiation which it is a part of but having an amplitude which rises from zero to a maximum and then decreases again, as shown in Figure 3.5. Note that this is not drawn to scale – the wavelength of light is around half a micrometre, not several millimetres. A typical light photon will actually consist of millions of wave 'cycles', so a highly magnified 'view' of a photon (if such a thing were possible) would look much more like a steady wave than can be shown in a diagram such as this.

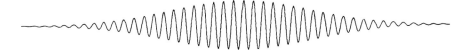

Figure 3.5 The Photon as a 'Burst' of Wave Energy

Study of the interaction of light with materials reveals that the energy carried by a photon is determined purely by its frequency. In fact it is directly proportional to the frequency, the two being connected by a universal constant known as Planck's constant, or h, which has the value of 6.6×10^{-34} Js. Remembering that the velocity of any wave is given by the product of its frequency and wavelength (λ), we may therefore write:

$$\text{energy of a photon} = h \times c/_\lambda, \text{ where c is the speed of light, } 3 \times 10^8 \text{ m s}^{-1}, \text{ and } h \text{ is Planck's constant.}$$

At long wavelengths these photons are so small that to all intents and purposes they form a steady stream, but at short wavelengths (high frequencies) they carry enough energy individually to do considerable damage to molecules and biological systems and the distinct nature of the 'bursts' of energy is very apparent. Visible light appears where it does in the spectrum partly because the photons carry just enough energy to tip the balance in the delicate chemistry of our eyes, without doing too much damage to the more robust molecules of everyday life.

For visible light, wavelengths range from approximately 0.4 to 0.7μm and photon energies from 5×10^{-19} J to about 3×10^{-19} J. These energies correspond to energy changes of individual electrons of roughly 2 to 3 volts, which is enough to produce a marked change of the behaviour of the electrons in some materials. (Compare a typical thermal radiation IR photon with a wavelength of 15μm and energy of 0.08 electron volts.)

The effects of visible light photons on the electrons in different materials may be classified from our point of view into:

- *Chemical*: an electron may be given sufficient energy to cause the breakup of the molecule it was part of, resulting in fading of dye colours, chemical changes in the silver compounds in photographic films, or dissociation of the active chemicals in the detector cells of the eye.
- *'Photoemission'* from metallic materials: although electrons are free to move around inside metals, they require a certain minimum amount of energy to escape from the body of the material. This energy is known as the *work function* (symbol *W*). If the energy of an incoming photon is greater than the work function of the metal, an electron may be ejected by the collision. Such liberated electrons are often described as *photoelectrons*, and the process is known as photoemission. This process is the basis for most image intensification devices.
- *Excitation of electrons*: in semi-conductor materials from localised orbits (the 'valence band') into a state where they are mobile, that is, available to be current conductors. This is known as photoconduction, and is used by photodiodes, etc., to detect and convert incoming light into a measurable current flow. Like photoemission, this can only occur if the incoming photon has sufficient energy to allow an electron to jump across what is known as the 'band-gap'.
- The above effects all entail the incoming photon giving up all its energy in a single electronic exchange. Often this is not the case, and the photon imparts its energy more generally as a localised deposit of heat energy thereby perhaps changing other measurable characteristics of the imaging surface (see especially pyro-electric detectors in the chapter 5).

(1)   CHEMICAL

       -    DYES
       -    PHOTO EMULSION
       -    EYE

(2)   PHOTOELECTRIC EFFECT

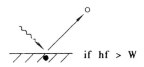

(3)   PHOTOCONDUCTION

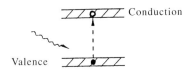

(4)   LOCAL HEATING

Figure 3.6 Effects of Visible Photons

Image Conversion

In order to transmit or relay an image it is necessary to convert the incoming stream of photons into a pattern of stored electrical charge which can be read out as an electrical signal. This is because the photons which build up the image are continuously arriving throughout the two dimensions of the image area. These photons need to be collected over a finite time and the resulting stored charges read out in an organised sequence. In practice this is achieved by representing the image as a series of scanned lines ('raster' scan), each representing the variations in intensity in a narrow strip across the image. This process is represented diagramatically in Figure 3.7. At the receiver, the picture is then built up on a display as the receiver regenerates the individual lines of the image in synchronism with the transmitting camera.

In order to create the impression of a continuous, realistic image of a changing scene it is necessary to display a succession of around 25 complete images per second (American signals use 30 per second). Owing to the nature of display technology, however, straightforward scanning of each line in turn throughout the image generates a most disturbing flicker between the top and the bottom of the screen. This is because the display phosphor gradually fades after it has been

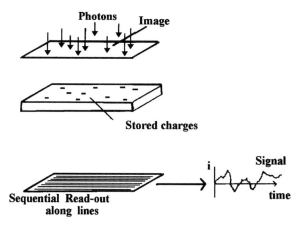

Figure 3.7 Electro-Optic Camera Principle

stimulated, which would result in alternating parts of the picture appearing brighter. In practice therefore, the image is scanned and displayed as shown in Figure 3.8, with first all the odd numbered lines being transmitted, followed by the even lines, so the whole screen area is 'lit up' with image information twice as rapidly.

Resolution

The detail available on the display is determined by the number of scan lines used vertically and by the maximum rate at which the electrical signal can vary as it scans along the picture lines. Current standard systems use a nominal 525- (US) or 625-line signal, in which there are actually rather fewer lines of video information. In order to provide approximately the same resolution horizontally and vertically, the standard signal band-width is set at 5.5 MHz, though it may be increased in non-standard systems to transmit or display extra horizontal detail.

As we saw in the previous chapter, the resolution of many systems is often quoted in terms of vertical bar charts, or effective TV lines (imagined as vertical), i.e., the number of light–dark cycles which can be recorded horizontally along a picture line. For a true comparison with the vertical resolution, the resulting value is often quoted, not as lines per picture width but instead as lines per picture height, i.e., per horizontal distance equal to the height of the picture. (It is worth noting that in order to display uniform image brightnesses correctly, even the best displays need a degree of overlap between adjacent scan-lines. This reduces the capability of the system to display vertical details also. A correction factor of around 0.7 is often used to allow for this.)

This discussion is based on the CCIR (European) standard shown in Figure 3.8.

This was intended for monochrome civilian television and subsequently adapted for individual national colour broadcast systems.

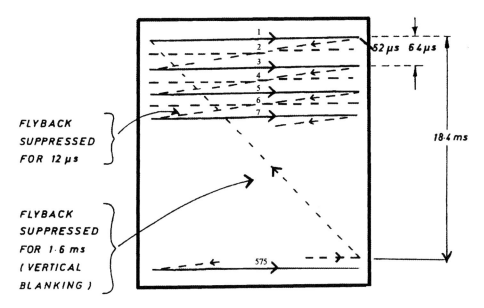

Main Parameters of a CCIR (Comité Consultatif International des Radiocommunications) TV System.

Lines per frame	6.25
(Active lines per frame)	575
Frames per second	25
Line interlace	2:1
Aspect ratio (width/height)	4/3
Video bandwidth	5.5 MHz

Note: The image is first scanned along the odd numbered lines 1,3____575 in 20 ms; this constitutes a field. The image is then scanned along the even lines, also in 20 ms. The two fields constitute a frame. There are therefore 25 frames and 50 fields per second. The picture is scanned in this way i.e., with 2:1 interlace, to reduce flicker.

Figure 3.8 'Raster' Pattern Image Scanning and CCIR Video Format

QUANTIFYING SYSTEM PERFORMANCE: MTF

The ability of an electro-optic system to relay fine detail with varying degrees of contrast can best be described quantitatively by a graph of the accuracy with which the system transmits contrast at different spatial frequencies. The Modulation Transfer Function (MTF) uses smoothly varying, sinusoidal bar charts covering the whole (useful) spatial frequency range, and describes the proportion

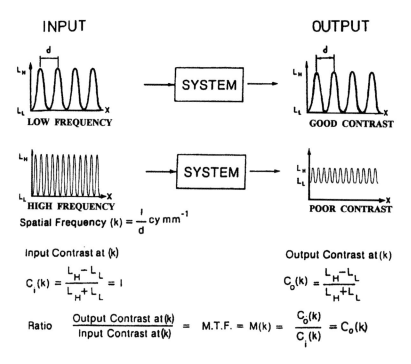

INPUT

OUTPUT

SYSTEM

LOW FREQUENCY

GOOD CONTRAST

SYSTEM

HIGH FREQUENCY

POOR CONTRAST

Spatial Frequency $(k) = \dfrac{1}{d} \, \text{cy mm}^{-1}$

Input Contrast at (k)

$$C_i(k) = \frac{L_H - L_L}{L_H + L_L} = 1$$

Output Contrast at (k)

$$C_o(k) = \frac{L_H - L_L}{L_H + L_L}$$

Ratio $\quad \dfrac{\text{Output Contrast at } (k)}{\text{Input Contrast at } (k)} = \text{M.T.F.} = M(k) = \dfrac{C_o(k)}{C_i(k)} = C_o(k)$

Input consists of a sinusoidal bar pattern of unit contrast and increasing spatial frequency. Output contrast measured at each spatial frequency. M.T.F. M(k) falls with increasing (k)

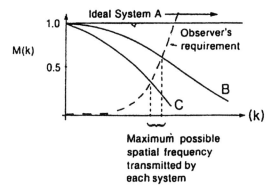

Maximum possible spatial frequency transmitted by each system

Figure 3.9 Modulation Transfer Function

of contrast transmitted at each frequency in the same way as we might portray the electrical frequency response of a hi-fi amplifier. This is illustrated in Figure 3.9, where low spatial frequency (large scale) variations are faithfully relayed, but more rapid variations lose their contrast because of system defects such as optical blurring. Note that the contrast definition used here, as with other electro-optic display systems where atmospheric scattering is not the prime cause of image degradation, is given by the difference of luminances divided by their sum (the same definition is used in thermal imaging, for the same reason).

An 'ideal' system could, perhaps, be imagined as having a 100 per cent response to all frequencies, though any practical system will have a finite limit to the frequencies it will transmit (if only diffraction). Indeed, there is a limit to the resolving power of the observer himself, which will set a useful limit to the detail required of the system. (Note that in practice MTFs are determined much more simply by analysing the spatial frequencies present in the output for specific complex inputs.) A typical MTF plot for one type of modern solid-state camera is shown in Figure 3.10.

TYPICAL SPATIAL RESOLUTION (White light)

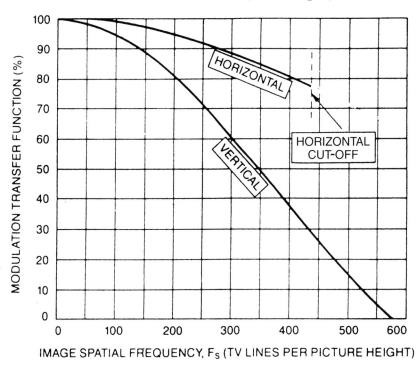

Figure 3.10 A Typical MTF

VIDEO CAMERA TYPES

Electro-optic camera systems may be divided into three main groups. As mentioned earlier, photons give rise to two electrical effects which may be used in detection systems. Conventional vacuum-tube technology developed two families of camera, the Vidicon principle based on photoconduction, and the

Orthicon family which used photoemission. Although still widely used in a variety of roles, the advent of cheap and increasingly good quality solid-state devices is rapidly relegating vacuum tube devices to specialised uses (such as studio TV cameras). Because of their robust, cheap and miniature nature, solid-state CCD cameras (see below) are increasingly widening the range of applications of daylight video systems and taking over the roles of the bulkier and more delicate vacuum devices.

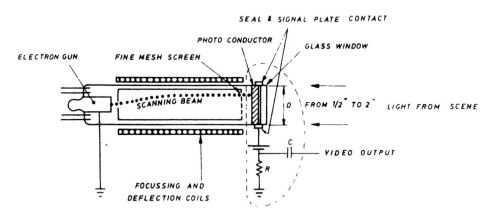

Figure 3.11 The Vidicon

Vidicon Cameras

The simplest (and cheapest) conventional TV camera system is known as the vidicon, and is shown in Figure 3.11. The image is projected on to a photoconducting 'target' situated at one end of a vacuum tube. The target converts the image into a pattern of stored charges which is then probed by an electron beam in the raster scan pattern outlined above. Scanning across the variations in stored charge in the target causes variations in current flow, creating the output video signal.

Several materials have been used for the target, with differing properties. The most commonly used targets currently are constructed from an array of silicon diodes. The resolution available from this system is acceptable for general purposes, but all vidicon cameras suffer from a tendency to produce 'picture lag'. The probe beam is required to neutralise the stored charge so that the next picture frame starts with a 'clean sheet' This is impossible to achieve in practice, and so the images which are read out have a tendency to preserve previous information superimposed on the current scene. This is particularly apparent with bright lights at night, and a familiar aspect of TV news reportage.

It is possible to combine the vidicon principle with a variety of image intensification methods giving a reasonably cheap, reasonably sized, moderate quality night vision system, albeit subject to picture lag problems.

Orthicon Cameras

The image orthicon is a much larger and more complicated camera than the vidicon, giving a high quality image in daylight conditions. In the orthicon incoming photons are focused on to a photoemissive material deposited on the inside of a large vacuum tube, causing electrons to be emitted (see Figure 3.12). The electrons are accelerated on to a target with sufficient force to cause the ejection of a number of secondary electrons, giving rise to an augmented positive charge. The target is then scanned with a precision beam whose current is amplified considerably by being channelled through a multiplier section.

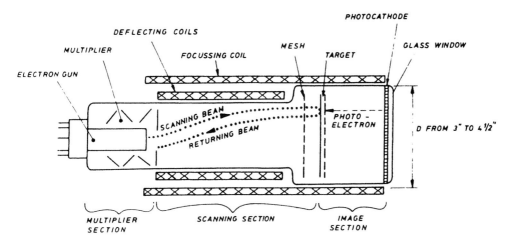

Figure 3.12 The Orthicon

From the above it may be seen that the orthicon is a substantial, expensive and delicate piece of equipment which can produce images of high quality in good light. In low-light conditions its signal to noise ratio is poor, and a modified version (the 'isocon') has been developed with a greatly improved low-light performance. This too can be aided with intensification to give performance down to very low light levels, but it remains a bulky, expensive and delicate piece of equipment.

The CCD Camera

As noted, any semiconductor material will generate mobile electrical charges when photons of the right energy fall on it, giving rise to a number of solid state devices for optical measurements. In order to develop an imaging system, a large number of individual detectors need to be set out in a two-dimensional array so that each minute part of a total image may be converted into an electrical signal. The key to the operation of a modern solid state camera is the application of charge-coupled device (CCD) technology (originally developed to act as a shift register to hold a sequence of data in a computer) to store and manipulate the charges generated by the incoming photons. See Figure 3.13.

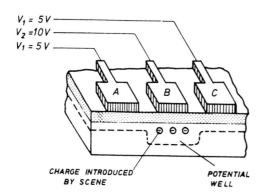

Figure 3.13 The Charge Coupling Principle

In a charge-coupled device, an array of electrodes insulated from the surface of a silicon chip is used to control electrical conditions within the body of the semiconductor. If one electrode is at a higher potential than the others, it will form a 'potential well' and trap nearby charges which are inserted or generated by incoming photons. Switching the voltages on neighbouring electrodes (as shown in Figure 3.14) can then be used to transfer all the stored charges to the next electrode in the array. This may then be repeated, causing the stored charge to move systematically towards a read-out buffer. In order to transfer the charges unambiguously it is necessary to have at least three electrodes controlling each element of data.

In a conventional 'frame transfer' imager, each picture element ('pixel') is thus represented by three electrodes, with the central one of each group starting at a higher potential and thus accumulating charges generated by incident photons for this portion of the image. After the appropriate collection time ($\frac{1}{50}$ s. for a single field), a rapid sequence of voltage switches is used to transfer the charges generated in the entire image through each column of electrodes and down into a storage area which is not exposed to light. This process, which involves a huge number of transfers, is carried out during the 'blanking period' while a conventional system is performing its 'flyback'. Because of the large number of transfers involved and the short time in which they have to be performed, the reliability of this operation is crucial in providing good quality imagery. The final step of the process involves the transfer of the charges one line at a time into a horizontal read-out register, at just the right rate to generate the lines of a standard video signal for the final output. See Figure 3.15.

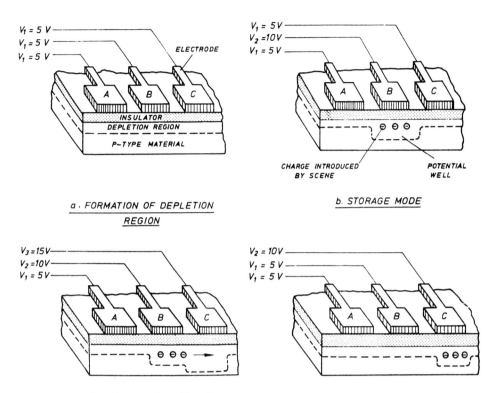

a. FORMATION OF DEPLETION REGION

b. STORAGE MODE

Figure 3.14 The Charge Coupling Process

In practice, a variety of problems arise which limit the quality of the final image. In a semiconductor material at room temperature, thermal energy is continually generating free charges which would normally eventually recombine and disappear. Here they are retained and treated as if they were a genuine part of the image, resulting in some inherent 'background noise' in the output picture. There is also a limit to the number of charges that a potential well of a given size can hold, limiting the dynamic range of intensities which can be recorded. Indeed, early systems responded very badly to wells overflowing, whiting out that area of the image as the charges spilled over ('blooming'), and generating unsightly vertical streaks during the readout process. This problem is now greatly reduced by incorporating overflow 'drains' to carry away excessive charges.

The large number of charge transfers required to read out the image also caused the image to be degraded, since it is not possible to transfer all the charges with 100 per cent efficiency every time. Early systems had around 99.9 per cent efficiency, but when this was repeated around a thousand times the result was a

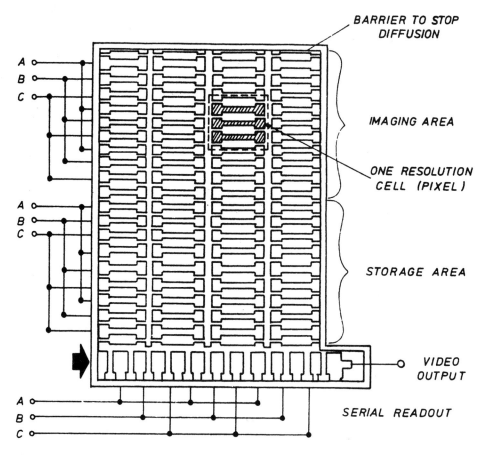

Figure 3.15 A CCD Frame Transfer Imager

very poor image. Modern, quality camera systems may have a r.m.s. transfer error of a few electrons in 10^6, resulting in an image which appears almost noise free. This may be further improved by slowing the readout process, but only in systems which can tolerate the reduced frame rate.

A further problem with frame transfer devices as described above is rather poor sensitivity, particularly at the blue end of the spectrum. This is because the light enters the device from above (in figures 3.13 and 3.14) and some of it is screened off by the gate structure. It is possible to erode the body of the silicon sufficiently to allow light in from behind instead, but this process is difficult to achieve reliably, is expensive, and results in much more delicate detectors since it involves the removal of much of the main body of the material. It does, however, allow the inherent sensitivity of the silicon to be properly exploited, with the result that cameras using this type of sensor can generate image information from very low-light levels, particularly if cooled and time is available to carry out all the transfers in the readout process slowly and precisely.

An alternative solution has been adopted by some manufacturers, which is to use a CCD array for the charge transfer process but to use an array of photodiodes as the actual detector elements (see Figure 3.16). This arrangement is known as an 'interline transfer' device, and is claimed to have a more even colour response and better anti-blooming characteristics than the ordinary frame transfer camera, at the expense of a somewhat reduced percentage of active detecting surface area ('fill-factor').

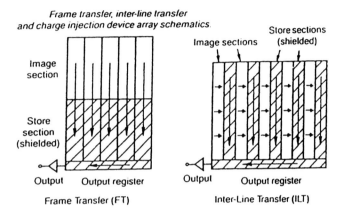

Figure 3.16 Frame Transfer and Interline Transfer CCD Cameras

Both of these designs may be extended to generate colour images and two strategies for doing this are in use. One alternative, the best but much the more expensive one, is to split the incoming light optically into separate red, green and blue images and provide each image with its own CCD detector. Alternatively, a single CCD imager may be used with a mosaic of coloured filters laid over individual pixels so that a local group, taken together, provides the colour information at the expense of resolution. One widely used array of colour-sensitive pixels is shown in Figure 3.17. Note that most of the filters used are not based on the red, green and blue required to pick up the individual colour components of the colour signal, since these would reject too much light. Instead, so-called secondary filters are usually used (magenta, yellow and cyan), together with one green element. The green is there because this is the waveband that the eye is most sensitive to, and it provides precise spatial information for the intensity part of the video signal. The colour information is extracted at lower resolution by comparing the outputs of the individual detectors within the block.

Although early CCD cameras suffered from poor resolution due to having only a modest number of pixels and poor quality due to the noise processes outlined above, improvements have been made at a remarkable pace (dictated by the

Yellow	Cyan
Magenta	Green

Yellow	Cyan
Green	Magenta

Figure 3.17 Colour Mosaic for Colour Filter CCD Cameras

economics of the boom in consumer electronics). Both the above formats of CCD camera can now provide reasonably priced, professional quality imagery, with a 'full video' (CCIR) specification of 575 lines of pixels and around 768 pixels per line using a detector just 8mm across. Even larger (high-resolution) arrays are available for specialist imaging systems, from 4096×4096 on a 50mm square chip upwards.

A further important development is the incorporation of 'enabling' and 'disabling' gates in the circuitry, allowing control of the length of time for which the detectors at each pixel are active. This permits the operator or an automatic circuit to control the effective exposure time for each frame, collecting extra photons if light is short or allowing very clear rapid 'snapshots' of fast moving objects in good light, enabling the basic camera mechanism to be controlled in a much more sophisticated way to achieve optimum imagery for given conditions.

IMAGE PROCESSING

So far we have considered a number of systems which are intended to help the observer see things which he would be unable to see clearly enough without help, either because they are too distant or because the imaging system is located in a different position from the observer. Electro-optics and electronics play an important part in this process, as witnessed by this chapter. So far, however, we have limited the discussion to devices which help the observer by detecting or collecting the available light more usefully, such as magnifying optics or remote, or long-range camera systems, which can detect more detail than the unaided observer is able.

In parallel with a steady advance in these technologies, which have evolved over decades, recent years have seen great advances in ways of processing images *after* they have been turned into a picture by some detection system (usually known as 'image processing' techniques, or, more grandiosely, as 'post-detection processing'). This development has come about partly owing to the greatly increased processing power made available by the computer revolution and partly in response to the increasing demands of sophisticated broadcast imaging and space-based observation technologies.

The technology now exists, indeed it is readily available, to *enhance* images which have already been generated so that the observer can see the things he needs to find more easily. Electronic technology has developed to a point where this can be carried out in real time, that is to say, the processing is carried out so quickly that the observer is able to see what is, to all intents and purposes, a 'live' scene, but watch an image which has been improved in a way which is going to help him carry out his task more easily and thus more reliably.

Some of this technology is already built into military and civilian imaging equipment, domestic camcorders are available which minimise the effects of sensor motion (due to inexperienced operators) by storing each image frame and recording it only after the position of the best digital match to the previous scene has been found, not to mention other 'edge-sharpening' or contrast enhancement options which may be available. On the military market, thermal imaging systems are prone to variation of sensitivity between one sensing element and another, and in-built processing is needed to compensate for this in 'live' video output.

Real-time image-enhancement systems have thus become available over recent years which act as plug-in modules between the sensor and the final observer, carrying out relatively simple but vitally useful roles, such as noise reduction, contrast stretching and edge enhancement. These are of obvious, immediate applicability in remote surveillance systems such as RPVs or remotely-guided

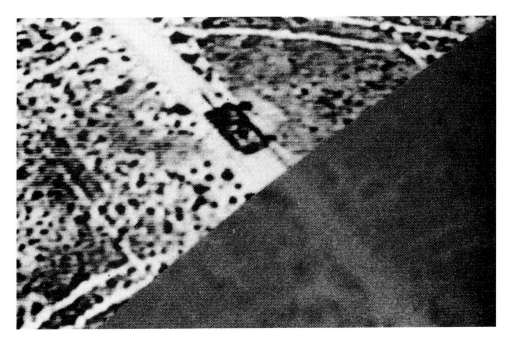

Figure 3.18 A Real-time Image Enhancement Compared with the Unprocessed Scene
(photo courtesy of Elbit Computers)

missile systems such as FOG-M, where the observer has no control over the system's environment and, in any case, has more pressing tasks to concentrate on than the detailed camera settings. The 'before' and 'after-processing' versions of the image from one such system are shown for comparison in the two halves of Figure 3.18.

More sophisticated processing makes possible a wide range of other battlefield systems, including alerting devices for air defence or battlefield surveillance, automatic target acquisition systems and video motion detectors for automatic and continuous monitoring of one or more points of special interest.

4

Image Intensification Systems

THE IMAGE INTENSIFICATION REQUIREMENT

The human eye has evolved to provide a powerful and remarkably versatile daylight sensor system with good resolution and an efficient colour discrimination capability. Under twilight conditions and below its ability to provide such detailed image information diminishes rapidly as there are insufficient photons to trigger the cone cell imaging system efficiently. Ordinary daylight imaging systems too have developed to collect the steady stream of photons from the scene and convert them into an electrical signal so as to provide image information such as colour or fine spatial resolution and accurate contrast discrimination with a reasonable degree of efficiency. By night the ambient illumination level is dramatically reduced, and with it the number of photons available for imaging systems. Low-light imaging systems thus introduce design requirements different from and more stringent than daylight systems, with particular stress on detector sensitivity and light-gathering power.

In the eye these problems are addressed by switching to the more sensitive, monochrome rod detection system, and by dilating the pupil to collect the maximum possible number of photons; but there is a further problem to be considered which dictates that the rod vision system has an inherently inferior resolution. This problem is known as *photon noise*, and it acts as a limiting factor, not just to the performance of the eye but of all low-light imaging systems. Because of the limited resolution capability of rod vision, the prime role of an image intensifier is to collect whatever light is available from the scene and generate an image which is sufficiently bright for the more discriminating daylight, cone vision to function.

We saw in Chapter 2 that levels of illumination by night may vary from 10^{-5} lux or below for overcast starlight through to around 100 millilux with a bright, full moon. A scene illuminated by, say, 10^{-4} lux, with an average reflectivity of 30 per cent will result in an object luminance of about 10^{-5} cd m^{-2}. For the observer to see useful detail in the scene, we need to aim to generate a final image with an apparent luminance of perhaps 1 cd m^{-2}, corresponding to twilight conditions. This would require an apparent gain in luminance of the order of one hundred thousand (10^5) with darker scenes requiring correspondingly more. The amount of gain we require thus depends on the conditions we expect to encounter. To put this discussion into context, Figure 4.1 depicts the probability of ambient illumination in north-west Europe exceeding a given threshold value. It shows that the probability of the ambient illuminance exceeding a low threshold such as 10^{-5} lux is very high (virtually 100 per cent), indicating that a system capable of giving good imagery at 10^{-5} lux would be unnecessarily expensive and elaborate for general use in Europe. In the vicinity of 10^{-3} lux (clear starlight conditions), however, the probability drops abruptly, from over 80 to around 50 per cent. This level of illumination thus represents a practical minimum requirement for general purpose, covert, use and is often taken as a useful point for specifying system capabilities.

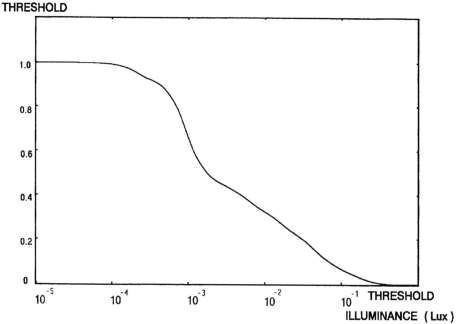

Figure 4.1 The Probability of Ambient Illumination exceeding a given threshold in NW Europe

In order to achieve the considerable amount of gain that is required by practical systems, the first step is to collect and focus as much light as is practical with a suitable objective lens, and convert the incoming photons into *free* electrons, which can then be manipulated to generate the necessary final image luminance.

This is done by imaging the scene on to a suitable sensitive surface (the *photo-cathode*), where the incoming photons in the image are converted to electrons by the *photoemission* process described in the previous chapter. The electrons are then either accelerated up to a high energy or multiplied hugely in numbers and projected electrostatically to collide with a luminescent screen (phosphor), from which visible light photons are released, to be viewed through the eyepiece. As each incoming photon triggers the emission of many thousands of photons at the final phosphor, the resulting image is much brighter than the original scene and is thus sufficient to activate the cone cells of the eye (Figure 4.2).

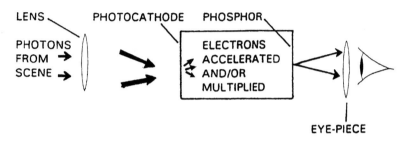

Figure 4.2 The Principle of Image Intensification

The Objective Lens and Photon Collection

The first part of the process is the collection and focusing of the available light. To maximise the performance of the system the aperture of the lens thus needs to be as large as possible, within the practical constraints imposed by the system role. General purpose night-vision goggles need to be reasonably compact and lightweight, and thus cannot use bulky lenses. Fortunately, they also need a wide field of view and thus may cause a short focal-length lens. Longer-range, higher-magnification weapon sights need larger lenses, but are associated with weapon systems which themselves are more substantial or vehicle-mounted. Thus an assault rifle sight such as the Common Weapon Sight, or CWS, has an effective objective aperture of 64mm, with a focal length of 116mm, giving an *f*-number of approximately 1.8. The stretched version, the 'Maxi-Kite', is illustrated in Figure 4.3 and has an increased ×6 magnification and a focal length of 198mm with a larger, 98mm diameter objective lens.

The Photocathode

The function of the photocathode is to convert the incident photons into electrons. The more efficiently this conversion occurs for a given type of radiation, the brighter and the more stable the final image will be. A wide variety of

Figure 4.3 The 'Maxi-Kite' Intensified Sight (*photo courtesy of Pilkington Optronics*)

materials have been tried to provide the most suitable response for night-vision systems, based around combinations of the very active alkali *metals*, caesium, sodium and potassium, with silver, antimony and other metallic and non-metallic elements. One particular combination of those three alkali metals together with antimony became known as S-25, and was found to give a particularly useful response to starlight illumination. Because of its good overall degree of sensitivity, peaking at the red end of the visible spectrum and extending usefully into the near infra-red, it was used almost universally for intensifier systems for many years and is still used today in many lower-priced systems.

Figure 4.4 shows the spectral response (the variation of sensitivity with wavelength) of a variety of materials used in optical detectors, including S-25, together with S-20, which has been widely used in daylight imaging systems. We noted in Chapter 2 that starlight illumination has a major component in the near infrared part of the spectrum. Systems intended to operate under low-light conditions can benefit greatly from using this extra, invisible ambient illumination which provides photons from the scene much like the visible signal. S-25 is thus far better suited to low-light conditions than S-20. An important side-effect of using a detector which responds to wavelengths above 0.8μm is provided by the fact that the chlorophyll content of natural vegetation has a high reflectivity at this wavelength and beyond.

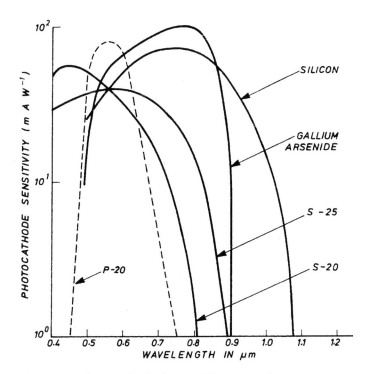

Figure 4.4 Photocathode Spectral Response Curves

Many ordinary materials reflect around 10 to 20 per cent of the visible light that falls on them (see Figure 4.5). The abrupt change to around 80 per cent at 0.8μm (the so-called 'chlorophyll edge') means that vegetation appears very bright when viewed through an image which responds to these wavelengths, and also that man- made objects and clothing appear particularly dark against them unless they too have been treated so as to make them IR-reflecting. Infra-red reflecting paint for vehicles and suitable camouflage fabrics are thus a necessity in situations where they may be observed through modern image intensifiers.

The response of gallium arsenide (GaAs) is also included in Figure 4.4. This has a markedly superior near-infra-red response and overall is about three times more sensitive to starlight than S-25. Its use in third-generation devices is responsible for their greatly improved performance. In recent years further work on photosensitive materials has resulted in photocathodes which respond even further into the near-infra-red to 1μm and beyond by 'doping' gallium arsenide with materials such as indium (indium gallium arsenide, or In-GaAs).

Also shown for reference in Figure 4.4 is the curve for silicon, which is used in daylight CCD detectors and appears to have a desirable long wave response. As a true semiconductor rather than a metal, its use in this type of intensification device is impossible at present, but progress in low-light CCD imaging systems may well give rise in the future to new, affordable night-vision aids capitalising on its greatly extended response.

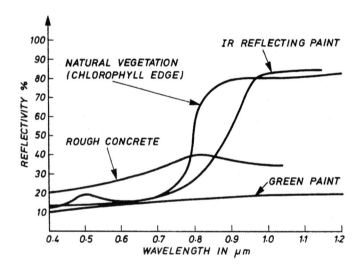

Figure 4.5 Reflectivity of Natural Vegetation etc.

GAIN MECHANISMS

As described above, there are two ways in which photoelectrons may be used to generate an image of increased brightness. The earlier approach, as used in first-generation intensifiers, was to accelerate each of the electrons drastically (typically through around 15kV), focusing them on to a phosphor screen, thus causing it to generate a substantially brighter image. Based on old, active IR systems, these devices were originally known as 'converter tubes', or 'inverter tubes' as they had the effect of inverting images (Figure 4.6). More recently, a method has been found to amplify the number of electrons at each point in the image using a large number of parallel amplification channels in a microchannel plate.

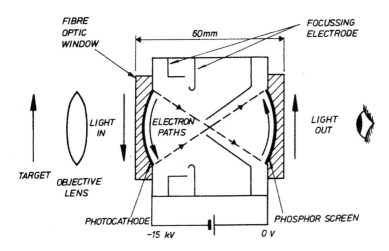

Figure 4.6 Single Stage Image Converter

A single converter tube gives a gain of around 50 and is thus useful only with active sources or where there is some background illumination or good moonlight, requiring illumination levels of between 10^{-1} to 10^{-2} lux. Such devices are currently widely available on the civilian market, but they are quite inadequate for the rapid detection and recognition of targets illuminated by starlight. To cope with such levels (10^{-3} to 10^{-4} lux) much larger gains are necessary, as we have seen. This could be achieved by coupling three single stages in cascade (Figure 4.7) by using high resolution fibre-optic windows. The gain for the three stages is typically about 60,000, taking the inevitable coupling losses into account, and the resulting imagery, although somewhat distorted, is remarkably clear, bright and stable.

The operating voltage of 45 kV is derived from an oscillator encapsulated with the intensifier and supplied from a low-voltage DC source. Automatic brightness control (ABC) with a fast response to sudden changes in scene brightness is necessary, eliminating 'white-out' effects common in early versions. Unfortunately, the total system, comprising three successive, modestly-sized elements, together with a long-focus objective lens and the eyepiece is inherently a bulky device, quite unsuited for use as goggles or even modern, lightweight weaponry.

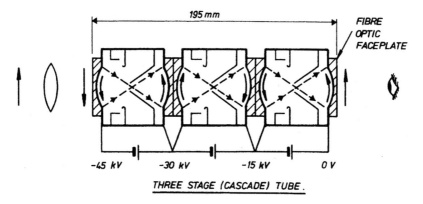

Figure 4.7 Cascade Tube Image Intensifier

SECOND GENERATION: MICROCHANNEL PLATES

Second (and third) generation image intensifiers incorporate a microchannel plate (MCP) to produce electron multiplication thereby achieving a dramatic reduction in build and weight but at the expense of increased noise. An MCP is an array of millions of minute hollow glass tubes (forming the individual 'channels') fused into a thin disc. Primary electrons from the photocathode are accelerated towards the MCP, and on entering one of the channels strike the wall and release a number of further electrons (see Figure 4.8). These secondary electrons are accelerated down the tube by the axial electric field caused by the voltage (around 1 kV) maintained across its length, and collide with the walls further down, generating more secondary electrons. This process is repeated over the whole length of tube so that finally a very large number of electrons emerge out of each channel and are accelerated on to the phosphor screen placed a short distance from the MCP. In this way the electrons from one part of the image are 'amplified' to form part of a much brighter final image. Electrons from other parts of the image are meanwhile also being 'amplified' independently as they travel through the channels corresponding to their part of the image. A complete microchannel plate is illustrated in Figure 4.9. The whole assembly of over a million channels operates on all the different parts of the image simultaneously, each channel contributing to its own part of the total picture.

The electron gain per channel, defined as the ratio of the output to the input current, depends on:

a. The applied voltage (Figure 4.10);
b. The length-to-diameter ratio of the channel (which affects the number of collisions);

c. The mean number of secondary electrons released at each collision, usually between three and four.

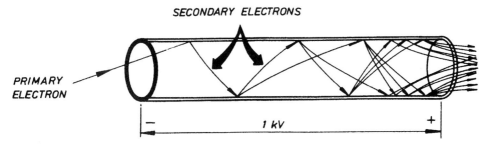

SECONDARY ELECTRONS

PRIMARY ELECTRON

−   1 kV   +

Figure 4.8 Channel Electron Multiplication

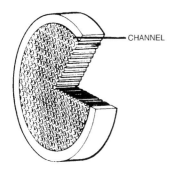

CHANNEL

Schematic Representation
of MCP

Figure 4.9 A Microchannel Plate

Because of (b) the diameter of the channels can be chosen to match the resolution required without affecting the gain. Typical values are 12μm for channel spacing, with a diameter of around 9μm, and a channel length (plate thickness) of about 0.4mm, giving a length to diameter ratio of about 40.

Figure 4.11 illustrates two types of image intensifier incorporating the MCP. The inverter tube is similar in action to a single stage of the cascade tube apart from the MCP. Electrons emitted from the photocathode are focused on to the MCP located in front of the phosphor, and after multiplication within the MCP are accelerated on to the screen where an erect image of the scene is formed. The proximity or wafer tube, in which the MCP is located immediately behind a flat photocathode, provides even greater saving in size and weight. Moreover, since the spacing between photocathode and MCP is about 0.5mm much lower voltages may be used as indicated, but at the expense of gain.

Two factors limit the maximum gain to about 4×10^4:

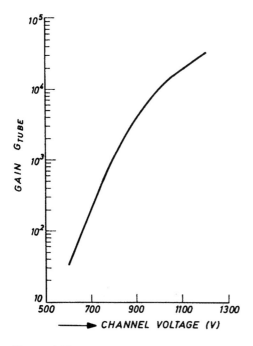

Figure 4.10 MCP Gain as a Function of Voltage

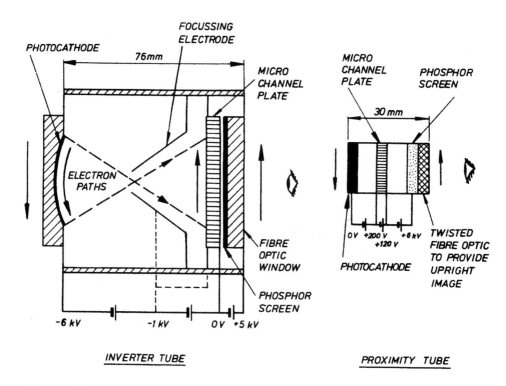

Figure 4.11 MCP Image Intensifiers

- The action of the MCP is linear, i.e., the gain is constant for a given applied voltage until the output current approaches the standing current of about 10μA that flows in the channel walls. The secondary electron current cannot appreciably exceed this because the walls would become positively charged, thus limiting or saturating the secondary emission current and hence the gain. This is the reason why MCP do not suffer from 'white-out'; a high light in the scene imaged on to a small area of the plate is suppressed by localised saturation in the affected channels.
- Molecules of gas locked in the glass during the manufacturing process are gradually released by the MCP in use and are then ionised by electrons. The positive ions produced are accelerated violently in the direction of the photocathode, releasing further electrons on the way, possibly leading to a discharge. The impact of positive ions on the photocathode causes bright scintillations and will cause considerable damage, limiting the life of the device.

Despite the great advantage of saving in size and weight and freedom from white-out, the original II devices incorporating MCP suffered from a number of limitations.

- In early second-generation devices tube life was somewhat limited, often to only around 2,000 hours of operational use because of the photocathode ion bombardment described above. Recently MCP systems have been coated with ion-absorbing materials, resulting in a four- or five-fold improvement in tube life.
- The final image in second-generation devices was twice as 'noisy' as cascade tubes (that is, the image appeared to 'flicker' badly). This is because of the variability of the gain of the MCP from one electron to the next (due to the uncertainty in both the generation of secondary electrons and the number of collisions). This problem made second-generation devices significantly less effective than the first-generation cascade tubes below starlight illumination levels. To counteract this they therefore tend to be used with rather lower gain settings. More recently, the development of enhanced sensitivity S-25 photocathodes, particularly the generation three GaAs systems, has compensated for this, producing dramatically better image quality.

A schematic view of the current Common Weapon Sight, or 'Kite sight' is shown in Figure 4.12. Proximity focusing results in a highly compact intensifier module at the heart of the design. The objective and focusing lens assembly may be seen projecting the image on to the photocathode at the front of the intensifier tube, and the phosphor at the rear of the tube is viewed direct through the eyepiece optics. Because the sight graticule is illuminated and can be switched on or off, it is not situated in the 'usual' position in a focal plane, where it would coincide with a focused image of the scene. Instead, it is located offset to the side and optically merged with the image of the phophor by a prismatic reflector. The whole device is thus relatively compact and lightweight and well suited to use both as a surveillance device and a light weapon sight.

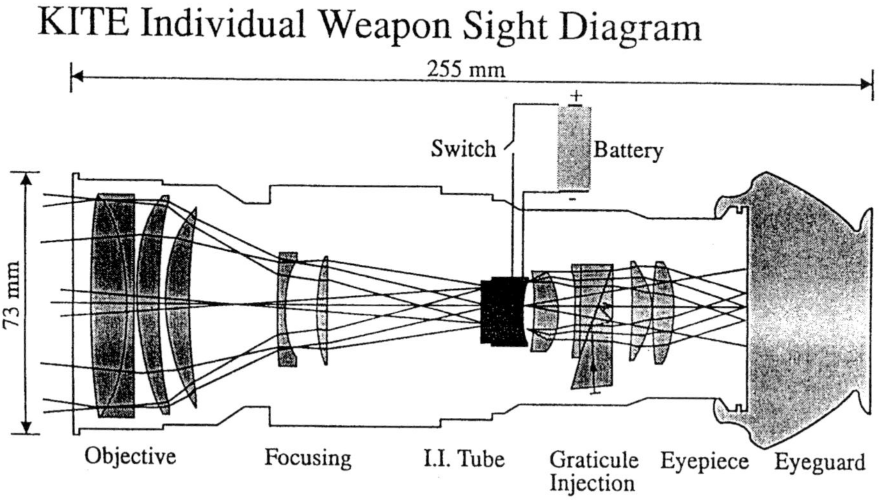

KITE Individual Weapon Sight Diagram

Figure 4.12 The 'Kite Sight' (Common Weapon Sight) *(by kind permission of Pilkington Optronics)*

Performance Limitations

The performance of any low-light device is subject to inherent limitations in that the scene is being represented by a reduced number of photons and the flow of photons is governed by statistical probabilities rather than regular certainties. This results in rapid fluctuations in the detected signal strength as successive periods of time turn up related but unequal numbers of photons. This variation becomes increasingly dominant as the flow of photons is reduced (the fluctuations are proportional to the square root of the average photon count, which becomes an increasingly large proportion for small numbers). This is illustrated in Figure 4.13, which shows how the *detected* signal fluctuates in time, even though the incoming light is nominally at a constant intensity. At reasonable light levels the detected signal fluctuations are only small (4.13*a*). For small signals however (see 4.13*b*), the result is a constant, relatively wide-ranging fluctuation.

In addition to causing each point in the image to flicker distractingly, these fluctuations also have the effect of masking differences in intensity between different (adjacent) parts of the image, thereby making it impossible to see details

Photons per Collection Time

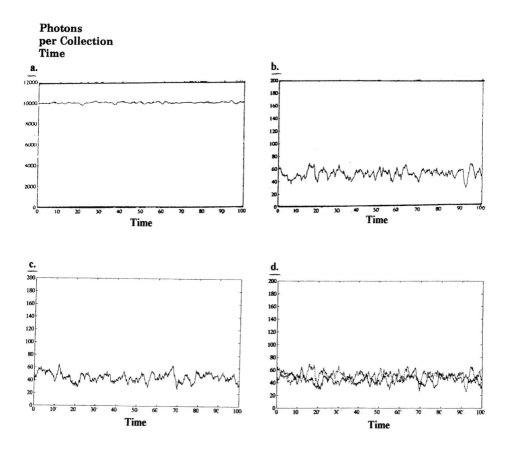

Figure 4.13 Detected Signal Fluctuations due to Photon Noise

or detect low-contrast objects. Figures 4.13*b* and 4.13*c* represent two, slightly different, low-level signals, with mean values of 50 and 45, respectively. They both show considerable fluctuations, and when the two are directly compared, as in Figure 4.13*d*, they overlap to such an extent that the observer cannot see that they are actually distinct values.

This phenomenon is known as *photon noise*. It is governed purely by the number of photons detected. As a result it may be shown that when photon noise is the limiting criterion, the finest spatial frequency observable through a device is proportional to contrast and the square root of the average brightness of the relevant part of the scene:

$$\text{Maximum spatial frequency} = kCL^{\frac{1}{2}},$$

where C is contrast, L is average luminance and k is the constant for a given system which depends on its detection and collection efficiency etc. A typical low-light performance graph for an electro-optic imaging device is shown in Figure 4.14, showing how at low-light levels its apparent resolution is severely degraded, particularly for low contrast objects. From a design point of view, therefore, it is clearly important to maximise the number of photons detected by increasing the objective lens aperture and transmission (within other constraints), and the detection efficiency of the photocathode, particularly for systems where it is important to see details at very low light levels.

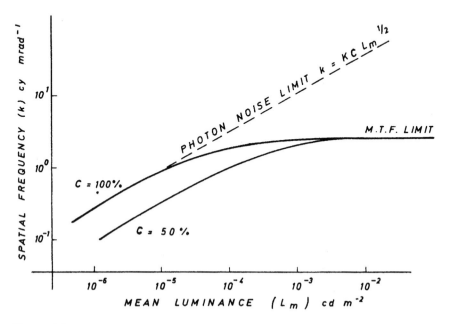

Figure 4.14 Variation of System Resolution with Object Luminance and Contrast

At higher light levels, the resolution limitation is inherent in the system design and construction. For a second/third-generation system the obvious limiting factor is the spacing of the channels in the microchannel plate, since the system clearly cannot relay details finer than one individual channel, and two lines of channels are needed to reproduce one line-pair of a test-chart. This problem can be tackled by making the microchannel plate larger (so the channel spacing forms a less significant proportion of the total image), and a variety of sizes are available, but a diameter of 18mm is the almost universal size in practical systems, and manufacturers and users are reluctant to make their equipment bulkier. The alternative is to make the channels finer and steady (but slow) progress is being made in this direction, with some manufacturers now offering tubes with a 9μm channel spacing.

In addition to this limitation, there are also limitations in the grain size of the phosphor and the photocathode structure which are also shared by first-generation devices; these also suffer from imperfect electron focusing, and the compounding effects of multiple, cascaded elements.

A further problem in the intensification of low-light images is the generation of free electrons at the photocathode which are not due to incident light but to thermal energy or background radiation (and indeed, also to nuclear contamination from any fall-out. These electrons produce a faint but steady background glow in the final image which reduces the contrast low-light scenes and obscures detail. This is illustrated in Figure 4.15. Manufacturers quantify this by measuring the resulting output brightness with no incident light, stating an equivalent background illuminance (EBI), that is, the photocathode illuminance which would produce this level of output in the absence of this effect. Clearly incoming light information at lower levels than this will not be seen, and it is desirable that this should be as low as possible.

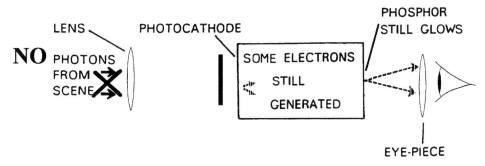

Figure 4.15 Equivalent Background Illuminance (EBI)

All these defects and limitations have been the subject of considerable research, culminating in enhanced second- and third-generation devices, as outlined above. Recent developments have resulted in still lower noise levels, and thus a steadier image and greatly enhanced tube life. As mentioned earlier, a number of improvements to photocathode materials have also been pursued, giving even better sensitivity either in the infra-red (for starlight applications or active, laser-enhanced or IR illumination systems) or in the visible spectrum for applications with low-level residual lighting.

In recent years a number of manufacturers have developed ultra-high gain systems based on hybrid or compound intensification, with gains of around half a million. For astronomical use, systems have been developed with multiple microchannel plates, multiplying up the gain correspondingly. This also has the effect of increasing the system noise dramatically, demanding long exposure times per frame or digital processing to enhance the resulting imagery. One current design for battlefield use utilises a third-generation initial section to give the highest possible sensitivity to night-sky radiation, followed by a further first-generation stage, increasing the gain without adding too much additional noise.

A great deal of progress has thus been made in improving all aspects of photocathode performance, and current weapon sights and goggle systems are available which can produce clear, good contrast and low-noise images down to starlight illuminance levels, together with a greatly reduced bulk. Nevertheless, image intensifiers are inherently dependent on the available light and are thus always subject to the operational limitations that this imposes. Many goggle systems incorporate an active infra-red source to enable tasks to be done with assisted illumination, and it is, of course, possible to use larger-scale active sources such as infra-red flood- and spot-lights, but these will naturally be visible to hostile observers who are similarly equipped. The development of stretched photocathodes which respond further into the infra-red also makes possible the use of longer wavelength light sources, such as battlefield laser systems. These are not 'visible' to most current intensifiers and offer a promising possibility for systems such as laser designation in addition to the exclusiveness of their current limited availability.

LOW-LIGHT TELEVISION

So far in this chapter we have been considering direct-view image intensifiers. The military requirement to operate a variety of indirect viewing, low-light TV systems down to starlight levels of illumination has led to a number of ways of

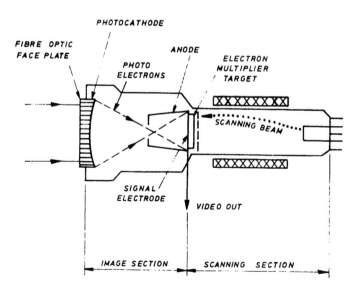

Figure 4.16 Electron Bombardment Vidicon

improving the low-light level response of the vidicons described in the previous chapter. These include:

a. Direct coupling to an image intensifier;
b. Enhancing target sensitivity through electron bombardment;
c. Coupling variant b to an image intensifier.

Direct coupling to intensifiers: this approach entails the direct coupling of a standard vidicon to a one-, two- or three-stage image intensifier or microchannel plate intensifier, though the coupling inevitably involves some loss of light and each additional stage reduces the MTF. They also tend to be heavy and bulky and only direct coupling to a MCP intensifier is considered worthwhile.

Table 4.1   Comparison of Typical Performance figures for LLTV

Parameter	Silicon Vidicon	SIT	ISIT	Image Orthicon	Isocon
image diagonal (mm)	16	25	25	45	35
typical faceplate illuminance (lux)	5×10^{-1}	2×10^{-3}	2×10^{-4}	2×10^{-1}	2×10^{-2}
corresponding scene illuminance (lux) ($F = 1.4$, $t = 0.9$, $r = 0.3$)	15 (very dark day)	6×10^{-2} (half moon)	6×10^{-3} (clear night sky)	6 (twilight)	6×10^{-1} (full moon)
resolution (TV lines per PH)*	700	750	550	750	1000
picture lag (3rd field) %**	8	10	10	3	3
spectral response	SI	S-20	S-25	S-20	S-20

Notes
* Resolution decreases with faceplate illumination; these camera tubes are limited by internal noise rather than photon noise.

** The target capacitance is the cause of picture lag in that it takes the electron beam a finite time to erase the accumulated charge. The lag is expressed as the percentage of the signal remaining after the lapse of three fields i.e., 3/50 s.

Electron bombardment vidicons: these consist of an image-forming section, similar to an image intensifier without its phosphor screen, built-in to the front end of a vidicon, as illustrated in Figure 4.16. Electrons, released from the photocathode and accelerated and focused on to the vidicon target generate large numbers of free carriers and therefore a much greater change in conductivity than occurs by photon action alone, as in the standard vidicon.

Silicon (EBSICON or SIT): by far the greatest sensitivity is obtained with a silicon target. Electron bombardment generates large numbers of electrons and holes leading to large changes in conductivity, such that the EBSICON is several 100 times more sensitive than a standard vidicon and has virtually eliminated all other variants. It is also known as the silicon intensified target (SIT) vidicon.

Intensified EBSICON or ISIT: still further low-light performance may be obtained by coupling direct to a MCP intensifier. For example, the ISIT (EBSICON or SIT plus MCP intensifiers) is capable of photon-noise-limited operation at the lowest light levels, although its use is limited by picture lag, as with other vidicon systems. Typical performance figures for such systems are shown in Table 4.1.

5

Thermal Imaging: Infra-red Systems

INTRODUCTION

The Latin prefix *infra* means below hence the infra-red (IR) region of the electromagnetic spectrum lies below the visible spectrum. The IR section of the spectrum is subdivided into the near IR (NIR) 0.7 to 3µm, middle IR (MIR) 3 to 6µm, far IR (FIR) 6 to 15µm, and the extreme IR (XIR) 15 to 1000µm. In contrast to visual, image intensifying and LLTV systems which use reflected energy, (sunlight, moonlight or starlight) thermal or IR imaging depends on emitted energy or emittance. Ambient light does not directly affect the detection of this energy. All objects with temperatures greater than absolute zero emit a continuous spectrum of electromagnetic radiation. For everyday hot objects most of this radiation lies in the IR region of the spectrum. To produce a thermal image the small temperature differences which exist in natural scenes are converted into a visual picture similar to that produced by a television with the important difference that no source of illumination is required so that thermal imaging is as equally effective by day or night.

The first military involvement with IR was during the First World War when it was investigated as a means of short-range secure communications. Considerable progress was made between the wars, particularly in the development of components such as detectors. During the Second World War both sides used IR communications and the Germans experimented with a tank fire-control system. Allied developments included the sniper scope or 'dark lightscope', often nicknamed 'Tabby'. Rapid progress occurred after the war in the development of devices suitable for detecting emissions from the exhaust plumes and hot surfaces of jet aircraft and by the late 1960s, emissions from objects at normal temperatures could be detected, provided that the detector was cooled to a low temperature. The achievement of appropriate low temperatures was solved by the development of the Joule Thomson mini-cooler and this made thermal imaging a technical possibility.

BASIC CONCEPTS

The Physics of IR Radiation

The main starting point for the analysis of imager design and performance is the radiation emitted from the scene. Any object, be it solid, liquid or gas whose temperature is above absolute zero (−273°C or 0 Kelvin) will emit electromagnetic radiation. If the object is in thermal equilibrium with its surroundings it simultaneously radiates and absorbs energy at the same rate in a form of a continuous spectrum of infra-red radiation.

Black-body Radiation

A black-body is one which absorbs all radiant energy incident upon it, regardless of wavelength. The radiation emitted by such a body is known as black-body radiation and depends only on the absolute temperature of the body.

Planck's Radiation Law

Planck's Radiation Law (1900) gives the spectral composition of the radiation emitted by a black-body at an absolute temperature T (Kelvin). The significance of the law is readily apparent when the temperature of various targets of military interest are plotted. See Figure 5.1. Thus it can clearly be seen that an MBT at, say 300K, gives off most radiation in the far IR.

It may also be seen from Figure 5.1 that the total radiant emittance (the area under the curve) increases rapidly with increasing temperature, and that each curve exhibits a maximum at a definite wavelength and that the higher the temperature the shorter the wavelength.

Planck's Law can be expressed as:

$$W_\lambda = \frac{C_1}{\lambda^5 \left[\exp\left(\dfrac{C_2}{\lambda T}\right) - 1 \right]}$$

Where W_λ = spectral radiant emittance ($W\ m^{-2}\ \mu m^{-1}$)
C_1 = first radiation constant ($2\pi hc^2$)
= $3.74 \times 10^8\ W\ m^{-2}\ \mu m^4$
C_2 = second radiation constant (hc/k)
= $1.44 \times 10^4\ \mu m\ K$
h = Planck's constant

c = velocity of light

k = Boltzmann's constant

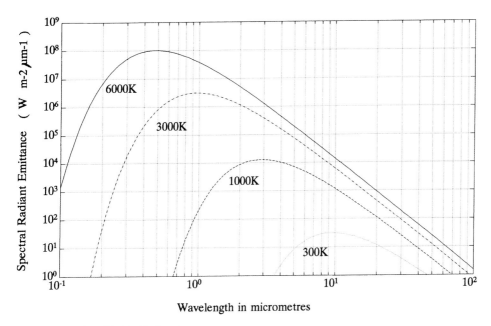

Figure 5.1 Planck's Radiation Law

Stefan-Boltzmann Law

If Planck's Law is integrated over all wavelengths the Stefan-Boltzmann expression for the total radiant emittance of a black-body at a given temperature is obtained:

$$W = \sigma \, T^4$$

Where σ = Stefan-Boltzmann constant

= 5.67×10^{-8} W m^{-2} K^{-4}

Wien's Displacement Law

If Planck's expression is differentiated with respect to wavelength and solved for the maximum, Wien's Displacement Law for a black-body is obtained:

$$\lambda_{max} \, T = \text{constant} = 2898 \; \mu\text{m K}$$

Where λ_{max} is the wavelength of maximum spectral radiant emittance.

So for $T=6000K$ (approximate temperature of the solar photosphere) $\lambda_{max}\sim1/2\mu m$, and for $T=300K$ (approximate MBT temperature), $\lambda_{max}\sim10\mu m$.

Emissivity

For real bodies, the radiation may be described by the inclusion of an 'efficiency' factor; this is called 'emissivity' and is given the symbol ϵ. The black-body is used as a standard and its emitting efficiency is said to be unity, i.e., its emissivity is one. The value of emissivity for a real body is therefore simply the ratio of the radiant emittance of the real body to that of a black-body at the same temperature. Real bodies therefore generally have emissivities less than unity.

Emissivity is a function of the type of material and its surface finish and vary with wavelength and temperature.

There are two types of real body:-

- the gray-body, where ϵ_λ is independent of λ. This is typical of solids;
- the selective radiator, where ϵ_λ varies with λ. This is typical of gaseous emitters.

To obtain the radiant emittance from a real body, Planck's Radiation Law is simply multiplied by the emissivity values. This may be seen illustrated in Figures 5.2a and 5.2b.

Some typical values of emissivity are given in Table 5.1.

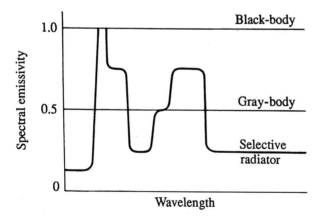

Figure 5.2 (a) Spectral Emissivities

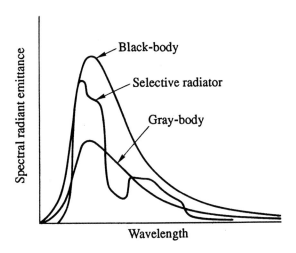

Figure 5.2 (b) Resultant Spectral Radiant Emittance

Table 5.1   Emissivity Values

Material	Emissivity
Aluminium	
polished sheet	0.05
anodised sheet	0.55
Brass	
polished sheet	0.03
heavily oxidised	0.61
Copper	
polished sheet	0.05
heavily oxidised	0.78
Brick	0.93
Concrete	0.94
Sand	0.90
Soil	
dry	0.92
wet	0.95
Wood	0.90
Human Skin	0.98

It is clear from these values that good reflectors (polished metals with reflectivities r ~ 1) are poor emitters of radiation since they have low emissivities, and that poor reflectors (heavily oxidised metals/human skin, etc.) are good emitters of radiation since they have high emissivities. This clearly indicates that the smoothness of the surface finish (with respect to the wavelength) plays an important part in the value of emissivity of a surface. (The low value of emissivity of polished copper is the reason why such kettles keep the water hotter for longer.) Provided there is little or no transmission of radiation through the material of the surface, then the following observation may be made:

$$\epsilon = 1 - r$$

The management and lowering of a target's surface emissivity may be seen to be the starting point for infra-red camouflage when the target is hotter than the background.

Thermal Contrast

A surveillance system detects the presence of a target as a result of contrast or some discontinuity in the background. Contrast occurs in the visible and near IR part of the spectrum because of variations in the reflectivity in the scene.

In thermal imaging, however, contrast is not simply a matter of the difference between the radiation emitted by a target and the background. As the emissivity of a real body is less than unity the surface of the body possesses a finite reflectivity and so the radiation leaving the surface of a target contains two components, namely a direct component controlled by the temperature and the emissivity of the surface, and the reflected component of the background and any neighbouring targets.

The radiation leaving the background is similarly affected by the presence of a target or targets and as a result it is difficult to predict the thermal contrast unless some assumptions are made.

Sometimes the reflected component dominates that emitted, this may especially be true in the case of objects at approximately 45° to the observer which reflect the cold sky above and hence give a negative contrast (for example, the windscreen of a Land Rover or helicopter canopy).

In general, the thermal contrast will depend on the emissivities of as well as the temperature differences between target and background.

An approximate value for thermal contrast may be obtained by considering the black-body case:

$$C = \frac{W_{Target} - W_{Background}}{W_{Target} + W_{Background}}$$

Now if $T_{Target} \approx T_{Background} = T$

$$W = \sigma T^4$$

$$C \approx \frac{\Delta W}{2W}$$

$$\Delta W = 4\sigma T^3 \, \Delta T$$

Therefore:

$$C = \frac{4\sigma T^3 \, \Delta T}{2\sigma T^4} = \frac{2\Delta T}{T}$$

For example: if the background were at temperature $T = 293K$, and the target were a future Soviet tank (FST), head on, gun not fired, then the perceived temperature difference may be only 1° i.e., $\Delta T = 1°$, hence the thermal contrast would be equal to only 0.0068 or 0.68 per cent, an inherently low-contrast situation.

TRANSMISSION

Transmission of IR Radiation through the Atmosphere

The transmission of IR radiation in the atmosphere is affected in the same way as is that of visible light: by absorption and scattering by molecules and by the presence of aerosols and particles. Of the two processes, absorption proves to be the more dominant at IR wavelengths, whereas scattering is the more dominant for visible light.

Figure 5.3 shows a plot of the percentage transmission against wavelength measured over a horizontal path length of about 1 nautical mile (1.9km) at sea level for a typical north-west European atmosphere. The plot results from the combined effect of molecular and aerosol scattering and absorption, but selective absorption by water vapour, carbon dioxide and ozone molecules are the dominant processes. This figure clearly exhibits several regions of high transmittance known as *atmospheric windows* separated by regions of high absorption. The principal windows that may be used for thermal imaging are 3 to 5µm and 8 to 14µm.

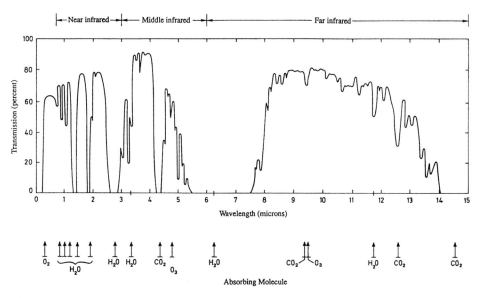

Figure 5.3 Transmission of a Typical Atmosphere in NW Europe for a 1 Nautical Mile Horizontal Path at Sea Level

Increasing humidity reduces the transmission within each window, though the 8 to 14μm window is more susceptible, and atmospheric humidities are generally greater in summer than in winter and therefore atmospheric transmission within the windows will be less in summer than in winter, particularly for the 8 to 14μm window.

From investigation of the contribution of the molecular absorption for typical summer and winter conditions, and the aerosol absorption and aerosol scattering for clear and hazy conditions for the two windows the following conclusions may be reached:

- transmission in the 8 to 14μm window is dominated by molecular absorption;
- transmission in the 3 to 5μm window is influenced more by aerosol scattering in summer and winter;
- for short ranges (less than 10km) the 8 to 14μm window appears to have the better atmospheric transmission for most circumstances;
- only in conditions of high humidity and extreme clarity in visual terms does the 3 to 5μm window have a superior transmission, particularly for ranges in excess of 10km.

Effects of Haze, Fog, Cloud and Rain

The transmission of IR radiation is superior to that of visible wavelengths, particularly if conditions are hazy or smoke is present. This is because the mean particle size of about 0.5µm is a relatively small fraction of the infra-red wavelength (say 10µm) and therefore any scattering by haze or smoke particles will be negligible.

Scattering by fog and clouds, on the other hand, is intense since the size of the droplets present range from 5 to 15µm. This is the reason for the poor performance of thermal imagers operating in either window when operating in fogs and heavy cloud.

Rain affects the performance of a thermal imager in two ways. It tends to reduce the thermal contrast of the scene by coating everything with a thin layer of water, and it affects atmospheric transmission in both windows almost equally, particularly in heavy rain. Attenuation in these circumstances may amount to as much as 20 per cent per km giving rise to only 33 per cent transmission over a 5km path.

IR SYSTEMS

System Elements

Each thermal imaging system will be designed to perform a specific task. Its components will be chosen to optimise system performance, for a particular wavelength region, and to maximise detectivity and resolution, depending upon the type of target environment. Regardless of the task all systems include the following components:

- optics: to collect the IR energy
- detectors: to convert the radiant energy to an electrical signal
- electronics: to amplify and process the signals
- display: to display a video signal for the eye

Optics

For IR optical systems, such as telescopes and missile domes, visible glass is unsuitable since it is optically opaque above ~2.7µm because of water-molecule absorption in the glass.

Alternative materials have to be used therefore, and these materials should have the following properties:

- optical transmission in the 3 to 5µm or 8 to 14µm window as appropriate;
- mechanical strength, resistance to thermal shock (in some applications) and high abrasion and rain resistance.

In addition, the lens material must be capable of being manufactured to produce aberration-free and colour-corrected optics. Most suitable materials have a high refractive index so special coatings are required to reduce the percentage of reflected radiation. Germanium is the most common material used in the telescopes of thermal imagers, it possesses a refractive index of approximately 4. This means that 36 per cent of the radiation is reflected at each surface and so with several surfaces the total transmission would be unacceptably small. It is essential therefore that anti-reflection (AR) coatings are applied to the optical surfaces. A family of coatings has been developed for use on external and internal surfaces. That used on external surfaces has a diamond-like structure of carbon which easily meets the requirements for high surface transmission, 94 per cent as against 64 per cent uncoated, and high erosion resistance.

DETECTION OF INFRA-RED RADIATION

IR detectors fall into two major categories depending on how the absorbed radiant energy interacts with the atoms of the detector material, namely thermal detectors and photon detectors.

Thermal Detectors

Thermal detectors operate as a consequence of the incident radiation heating the surface of the detector material. This causes an associated rise in temperature of the detector material, and, as the material selected has some temperature dependant property (such as resistance), then this property changes to yield an output (typically electrical) proportional to the level of incident radiation. Examples of thermal detectors are the thermocouple, thermopile, thermistor, bolometer and pyroelectric detector.

The response of a thermal detector tends to be independent of wavelength if the detector is perfectly black, because the detector simply requires a certain amount of energy to cause a rise in temperature regardless of what wavelength that energy is. The response also tends to be rather slow because of the inherent thermal capacity of the detector. The slow response of such detectors limits their ability to deal with rapid changes, for example moving targets, and with the exception of the pyroelectric detector, thermal detectors are generally unsuitable for thermal imagers. The inherent thermal capacity also means that the thermal detector is generally much less sensitive than a photon detector (typically 100 times less sensitive).

The thermal detector does have one major advantage: that because the very property being observed is temperature dependant, then the detector does not generally require cooling, and, indeed, such cooling may destroy the detector's ability to perceive the signal. This attractive feature means that such detectors are likely to be used in the next generation of rifle sight, when coupled with two-dimensional read-out technology (see later).

Photon Detectors

In a photon detector there is a direct interaction between the incident photons and the electrons of the detector material. The response of the detector is proportional to the number of photons absorbed. There are two types of interaction possible: the photo-emissive effect and the internal photo effect.

The photo-emissive effect in which electrons are released from a photocathode into a vacuum is described in Chapter 4. It is unsuitable for detecting middle and far IR radiation, since the photon energies in this region of the spectrum are too small in comparison with the work function of any available photocathode.

The internal photo effect may be characterised by a photon-electron interaction, where the photon energy is transferred to an electron in the valence band of the detector material. This energy promotes the electron across the material band gap into the conduction band, leaving behind an electron vacancy or 'hole', which behaves much like a positive charge. This is represented diagrammatically in Figure 5.4. The response of such a detector is extremely fast compared with a thermal detector's since the thermal capacity is not involved.

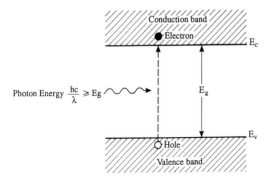

Figure 5.4 Internal Photo Effect

If the energy of the photon incident on the photon detector is smaller than the band gap, then the electron will not be promoted across the gap, hence such detectors have a long wavelength cut-off limit beyond which they will not respond. This may be given by:

$$\text{photon energy} = \frac{hc}{\lambda_c} = E_g$$

Where λ_c = long wavelength cut-off limit
E_g = band gap energy

Therefore to detect photons of different wavelengths, materials with different band gaps are required. A list of photon detectors, and their cut-off limits are given in Table 5.2.

Table 5.2 Photon Detector Materials

Material	Symbol	Cut-off Limit (μm)
silicon	Si	1.1
germanium	Ge	1.65
lead sulphide	PbS	3.1
indium antimonide	InSb	6.2
cadmium mercury telluride (CMT)	CdHgTe	12.3

Therefore indium antimonide may be used as a detector for the 3 to 5μm band and the alloy CMT may be used to cover the 8 to 12μm region of the 8 to 14μm band.

The internal photo effect may be further divided into two forms: photo-conductive (PC) and photo-voltaic (PV): in the photo-conductive type the detector material is generally pure 'intrinsic' material, and the electron excitation across the band gap increases the detector material's conductivity; in the photo-voltaic type the detector is made of a 'p-n' junction of the detector material, and the electron excitation across the gap causes a change in the voltage generated across the junction.

Cooling

As the photon wavelength increases, the band gap of the detector required decreases. This leads to a problem in that an increasing number of electrons have sufficient energy (thermal energy due to the temperature of the detector material) to cross the band gap between the valence and the conduction band. These thermally-excited electrons are a prime source of detector noise, and may readily swamp the photon-generated signal as the required band gap gets smaller and smaller. The obvious solution to this problem is to cool the detector material such that the electrons no longer possess the thermal energy to cross the band gap. In general, the smaller the gap, the greater the level of cooling required.

The most commonly used cooler in contemporary thermal imaging systems is the Joule Thomson mini-cooler, or JT cooler. The Joule Thomson effect arises when a gas is allowed to expand and consequently cools down. The most readily available gas is air. This is dried and compressed (typically to in excess of 300 atmospheres pressure). The compressed gas is then fed into the Joule Thomson cooler, which is a spiral counterflow heat exchanger with a small hole at the end. This spiral is inserted into the precision glass bore of a vacuum dewar. As the gas expands and cools at the end of the spiral it is forced by the bore to pass over the spiral counterflow heat exchanger on its way out, cooling the spiral as it does so. The gas now travelling down the spiral is therefore slightly cooled by the time it reaches the end, where it expands and cools some more. This process continues until the temperature at the end of the spiral reaches approximately –196°C (77 K), or liquid nitrogen temperature (the major component of air). A small 'puddle' of liquid nitrogen is therefore formed at the end of the spiral, and the detector material, which is situated on the other side of the glass bore, therefore reaches approximately 77 K. The vacuum dewar reduces the heat transport problems of the outside air, and the window material on the front of the dewar is generally made of germanium. This JT cooler is depicted in Figure 5.5. Typical cool-down times are of the order of tens of seconds, depending on the application of the thermal imager, but some coolers have been fabricated with cool-down times of the order of a second or less.

Another type of cooling technique becoming popular is the Stirling cycle cooler. This is an enclosed reservoir of gas (generally helium) which has a compression space and an expansion space. The compression space gets hot; the

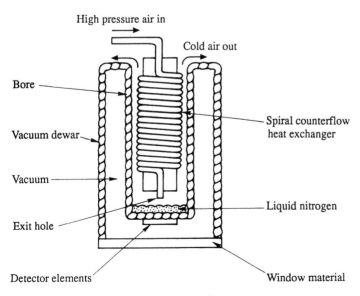

Figure 5.5 Joule Thomson Mini-Cooler

expansion space gets cold. These Stirling engines typically require 20 watts of electrical power and take several minutes to cool down. This is not generally a problem for airborne or shipborne usage, but clearly may be a severe restriction for hand-held systems which may require quick-into-operation times.

THERMAL IMAGING SYSTEMS

Complexities

When designing a thermal imager one is therefore faced with a two-edged problem. Infra-red detector arrays and their associated cooling systems are difficult and expensive to fabricate, and the more complex the detector array the greater the electrical complexity associated with them. Therefore one may choose a 'simple' detector array, at smaller cost, requiring simpler electronics, but requiring a 'scanner' which itself may be complex and expensive.

Single Element Scan

The simplest detector is obviously a single element. This is focused via a lens on to the scene in 'object space'. The motion of two mirrors combines to scan the element across the scene in both vertical (elevation) and horizontal (azimuth) scans (see Figure 5.6). As only one element is 'viewing' the scene it is sampled in time to give a number of picture points (typically 10,000 as a minimum) and this

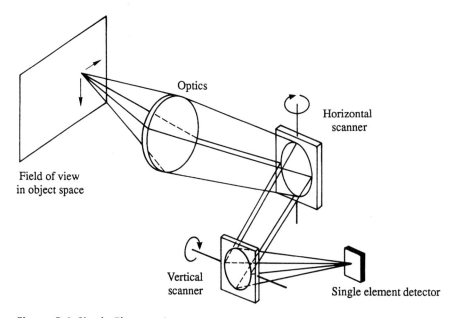

Figure 5.6 Single Element Scan

picture must be presented to the eye at a pleasing rate (typically 25 times a second or quicker to avoid flicker).

This means that the scanning system will be moving very fast, and that the time for which the detector views any part of the scene (the stare time) is very short. This in turn means that the detector receives only a small signal from any part of the scene and hence it produces a thermally insensitive picture with a poor signal to noise ratio.

The fast scan speed also means that the scanner itself may well be mechanically difficult to fabricate, especially its bearings and motor, and be expensive.

The relative insensitivity of such a device means that it is rarely used in military surveillance systems, but may be found in both commercial and medical imaging systems.

Parallel Scan

Here the scene is scanned by a number of detector elements mounted in a vertical array (see Figure 5.7). Each horizontal sweep of the scanner now produces as many lines of picture data as there are detector elements in the array. This allows for a much lower scanning speed for a given data rate, meaning a longer stare time and an increased signal to noise ratio. (It should be noted here that the use of a detector array with N elements improves the signal to noise ratio by a factor of $\sqrt{N}$, because the stare time increases by N, therefore the signal increases by N, but the noise which is random and incoherent increases only by $\sqrt{N}$.)

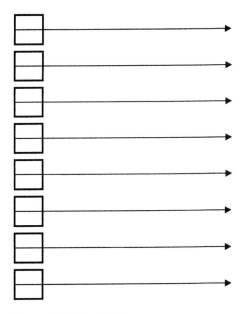

Figure 5.7 Parallel Scan

The performance from each detector element and its associated processing/amplifying electronics must be uniform or calibrated out (gain and offset adjustment), otherwise a 'streaky' picture would result.

In general this non-uniformity in detector response may limit the length of the array. Current in-service systems of this type have typically a few tens of elements in the array.

To obtain more lines of resolution in the picture it is then necessary to incorporate some form of vertical scan as well. This is generally done in steps or 'swaths', where the array is first scanned across the scene horizontally in one swath, then the vertical scanner steps down, and the array is scanned across a second 'lower' swath, and so on.

One method of achieving this is again to use two separate mirrors, a fast rotating horizontal scan mirror, and a slower 'nodding' vertical mirror. Another method is to use a rotating mirror with multiple mirror facets at varying elevation angles corresponding to each swath (see Figure 5.8).

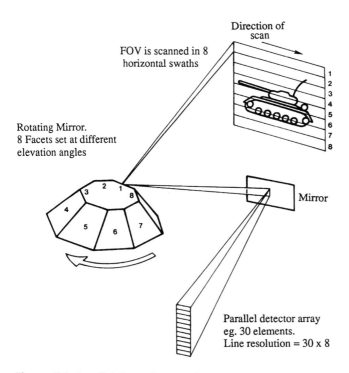

Figure 5.8 Parallel Scanning Mechanism

Future systems may well have arrays of hundreds of elements (called a long linear array) and produce a picture in only one or two swaths. The picture quality from such a device is likely to be very high.

Serial Scan

Again the scene is scanned horizontally across a number of detector elements, but this time the detector elements are also mounted horizontally (see Figure 5.9). It may be seen that the information from the scene will pass over each successive detector after a short time delay dependent on the scan speed. If the signals from the individual detector elements are added together (with the appropriate delay being added electrically), then for an array of N elements, obviously the magnitude of the signal would increase by a factor of N, and once again the noise would increase by $\sqrt{N}$, yielding a signal to noise improvement of $\sqrt{N}$.

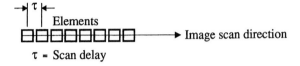

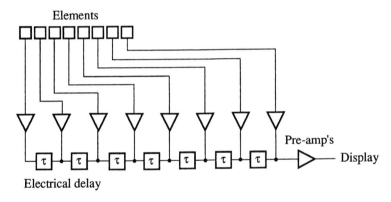

Figure 5.9 Serial Scan

This serial integration also helps to average out any element to element non-uniformities, but has the disadvantage of the greater electrical complexity.

Serial scan on its own would simply yield an effectively more sensitive single detector which would have to be scanned at the same rate as the single detector system, therefore arrays combining both serial and parallel elements have been fabricated, and this is obviously called *serial–parallel scan* (see Figure 5.10). This system is now electrically quite complex, and it is difficult physically to get electrical interconnections on to the innermost detector elements.

These difficulties have lead to the development of the SPRITE detector array.

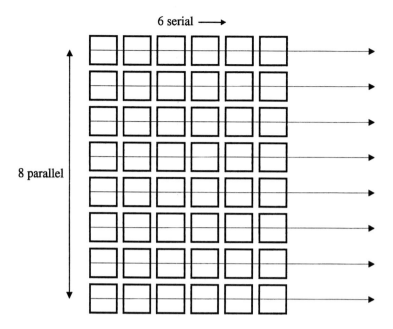

Figure 5.10 Serial-Parallel Scan

SPRITE Array

In the SPRITE an element is fabricated which is typically about ten times as long as it is wide. The detector material is biased with a current source; this causes the mobile carriers generated by the infra-red radiation to 'drift' towards the read-out zone. If the drift speed is matched to the speed at which the scene information is being scanned across the SPRITE, then all the carriers associated with a particular part of the scene arrive in phase at the read-out region, giving an effective $\sqrt{N}$ increase in signal to noise ratio (where N is approximately the length of the SPRITE divided by the width). This is a great saving in terms of electrical complexity and interconnection difficulty compared to the standard serial scan (see Figure 5.11).

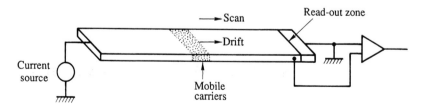

Figure 5.11 SPRITE Detector Element

In the SPRITE array a number of SPRITEs are mounted vertically to give parallel scan. These arrays are the basis of some of the best currently available thermal imaging systems.

Two-Dimensional Staring Arrays (Focal Plane Arrays)

If two-dimensional staring arrays can be fabricated with large enough numbers of elements, there would be no need for a scanning system. This would have several major advantages and disadvantages compared with a scanned system.

Advantages

No scanner would mean:

- mechanically less complex;
- potentially a lower power requirement because there is no scan motor required;
- environmentally more rugged (no mechanical device to break down under shock/stress).

Stare time:

- provided the electronic read-out of the data from the two-dimensional array is 'fast', then a two-dimensional system has the ability to 'stare' at the scene for almost a complete frame time compared with the short 'stare' time of a scanned system. If the 'stare' time is increased by a factor N, then once again the signal-to-noise ratio would improve by $\sqrt{N}$. Hence a fully-staring, two-dimensional array will inherently be much more sensitive than a scanned system with the same effective picture format.

Disadvantages

Detector more complex:

- electrically more complex;
- many physical electrical connections to many detector elements (lead-outs) means difficult fabrication techniques;
- many more detector elements means the element-to-element non-uniformities become even more severe requiring greater electronic correction to be carried out on the raw data, hence more expensive, complex, and power-hungry electronics.

However, the lead-out problem has been overcome by the integration of a silicon charge coupled device (CCD) with the infra-red detector element. If the detector material is not of the same crystalline structure as silicon (for example a CMT detector element), then this is called 'hybridisation' (or Z plane technology in the USA). The CCD acts as a store for the charge generated in the infra-red detector material when the detector is 'staring' at the scene, and also acts as the read-out device when operating in the 'transfer mode' (see Chapter 3). One element of this hybrid structure is shown diagrammatically in Figure 5.12.

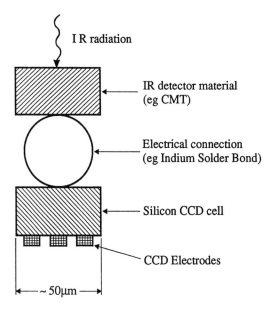

Figure 5.12 Hybrid Stucture of 'One' Element in a Staring Two-Dimensional Array

Current limits on the size of these photon detector two-dimensional arrays depend on the detector material, but indium antimonide arrays of 256×256 are commercially available, and 512×512 is available at a price.

THE FUTURE OF THERMAL DETECTORS?

It should be mentioned at this point that a silicon read-out structure may be used in conjunction with a pyroelectric material (a thermal detector), and that this is the basis of the future rifle sight mentioned earlier in this chapter. Currently such devices are the subject of intense R & D in both the UK and the USA, and when produced in sufficient quantity may eventually be as cheap as Generation 3 image intensifiers.

OTHER SYSTEMS

Remote Ground Sensors

Several types of intruder alarm use single-element thermal detectors to detect the presence of a radiating object. In military systems they are generally used in conjunction with acoustic or seismic sensors. Commercially available 'security lights' use a single-element thermal detector to switch the light on when a radiating object enters the field of regard.

Infra-red Line Scan (IRLS)

IRLS is an airborne system used in reconnaissance aircraft and unmanned aerial vehicles to supplement conventional photography and give a night capability. The motion of the airframe provides the scan in one direction; mechanical scan in the form of a rotating prism or mirror is used to scan across the line of flight. The signal from the infra-red detectors is used to drive a scrolling display, or a video data recorder for analysis at a later time.

Missile Guidance

Infra-red homing or heat-seeking missiles have been in service for many years. A suitable infra-red detector, usually operating in the 3 to 5µm waveband for aerial targets, 'locks on' to the primary source of emission, usually the exhaust plume and very hot engine parts of the target. The output signals from the detector are fed to the control surfaces on the missile and are used to guide it to the target. Some of the latest generation of infra-red homing missiles have a full imaging capability via either a scanned array or a staring two-dimensional array (these seekers are generically referred to as imaging infrared I^2R). These I^2R systems are remarkably capable and are extremely difficult to decoy away from the target.

Infra-red Search and Track (IRST)

IRST are generally systems that scan a large field of regard (up to full 360° in azimuth). When an IR target is detected the IRST simply alerts the operator of its presence and continues to track it. Most IRST systems do not generally present the operator with a full TV compatible picture of the target. Such systems may operate in either or both of the 3 to 5µm and the 8 to 14µm waveband.

SUMMARY

The field of infra-red continues to progress rapidly. Thermal imaging systems are continuing to be developed to give better spatial and thermal resolutions. Future systems are likely to be either parallel-scanned, long linear arrays or fully staring two-dimensional arrays; either system will enable acquisition of targets at greater ranges than current systems.

The thermal imager is a passive system which does not rely on ambient illumination and is therefore just as capable by night as it is by day. Under clear atmospheric conditions the thermal imager will usually outrange visual surveillance systems and will penetrate most battlefield smokes, haze and light mists. However, fog and rain, where the droplet size approaches or exceeds the infra-red wavelength, will cause severe scattering and will reduce the thermal range to little better than that of the visual range. Under these weather conditions the thermal imager would require complementing by a radar system which is less affected by fog and rain.

6

Laser Systems

Since laser action was experimentally confirmed in 1960, it has found use in a wide range of applications in the defence, industrial and medical fields. Its unique properties have made it a very important tool for the acquisition and surveillance of military targets, particularly in the ranging and designating roles, and its effectiveness in the precision aiming of air-to-ground munitions has been amply demonstrated in operational scenarios.

The aim of this chapter is to describe the main features of lasers, the principles of laser operation, the lasers and the techniques which are being deployed in target surveillance operations and the applications themselves.

UNDERLYING PRINCIPLES

Features of Lasers

Lasers are devices that generate or amplify coherent radiation at wavelengths (frequencies) in the infra-red, visible and ultraviolet regions of the electromagnetic spectrum. They extend the principle of *stimulated emission* demonstrated earlier at microwave frequencies (MASER action) to the optical frequencies and hence given the name LASER (light amplification by stimulated emission of radiation).

There is a close correspondence between MASER and LASER action in the areas of coherent signal generation, amplification, modulation, transmission and detection. The laser, however, works at a much higher frequency (shorter wavelength), giving it enormous advantages over the microwave technique in source intensity, beam collimation, ultrashort pulse widths and superior target identification. Against these advantages the laser beam does not propagate through the atmosphere in poor atmospheric conditions as well as a microwave beam. Systems will often deploy both techniques in implementation, making use of microwaves to acquire the target and the use of the laser to identify and track it.

To give some idea of performance levels, a pulsed Nd:YAG laser can produce a peak power density of 10^{18} W m^{-2} and a continuous wave CO_2 laser an average power density of 10^{13} W m^{-2}; some 10^7 and 10^2 times, respectively, that from an arc plasma, the most intense non-coherent, optical source.

The frequency stability or, in optical terms, the degree of monochromaticity, for a highly stabilised, continuously working laser can be as high as one part in 10^{13}, greatly exceeding the spectral purity of other optical sources.

The divergence of the output laser beam is measured in terms of milliradians for tactical applications: strategic applications are measured in terms of nanoradians. These are highly collimated relative to the MASER. To achieve the beam divergence from a laser telescope 10^{-2}m diameter would require a microwave antenna some 200m in diameter. This high degree of directivity enhances covertness and makes countermeasures much more difficult to deploy against the laser.

Laser pulse widths can be made as narrow as 10^{-12} s, though tactical applications utilise lasers of pulse width 10^{-8} s. Those lasers based upon certain organic dyes or, to a lesser extent, the solid state and semiconductors can be tuned over wide wavelength ranges resulting in important tactical advantages over fixed-wavelength lasers.

Though lasers suffer from optical noise because of the unavoidable presence of spontaneous emission within the laser medium, the application of heterodyne detection, following microwave practice, can reduce this by two orders of magnitude.

Lasers are not particularly efficient in converting input power to coherent radiation. For example, the optically pumped Nd:YAG laser has a conversion efficiency of only a few per cent. The semiconductor injection laser and the CO_2 TEA laser are some ten times more efficient and excimer lasers are also in this category.

Table 6.1 illustrates where the lasers fit within the electromagnetic spectrum and identifies particular laser types of interest.

Principles of Laser Operation

Basic Characteristics

Laser light is distinguished from ordinary light in that it is coherent; that is to say, composed of wave trains of near identical wavelength vibrating in phase with each other. This feature results in a very intense, highly monochromatic and highly directional beam of radiation. The difference between laser light and that from a torch is illustrated in Figure 6.1.

Table 6.1 Lasers as Part of the Electromagnetic Spectrum

Wavelength (metres)	Electromagnetic radiation	Typical laser emitters	
		Wavelength (nm)	Laser type
10^{-12}	Gamma rays	308	Excimer xenon chloride
10^{-11}		488-515	Argon
10^{-10}	X-rays	532	Neodymium YAG (frequency doubled)
10^{-9}		590	Rhodamine 6G
10^{-8}		633	Helium neon
10^{-7}	Ultraviolet	694	Ruby
10^{-6}	Visible	700-815	Alexandrite
10^{-5}	Infrared	850	Gallium arsenide
10^{-4}		1064	Neodymium YAG
10^{-3}	Millimetre waves	1540	Erbium
10^{-2}		1540	Neodymium YAG (Raman shifted)
10^{-1}	Microwaves	2060	Holmium
1		2500	Hydrogen fluoride
		3800	Deuterium fluoride
		10600	Carbon dioxide

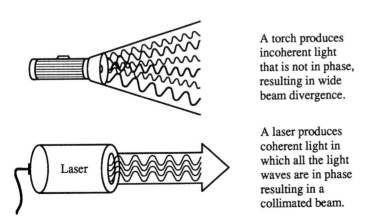

A torch produces incoherent light that is not in phase, resulting in wide beam divergence.

A laser produces coherent light in which all the light waves are in phase resulting in a collimated beam.

Figure 6.1 Difference Between Ordinary (Incoherent) Light and Laser (Coherent) Light

Basic Elements

The basic elements of a laser are an active medium having suitable optical characteristics, a source of energy to pump the medium, and an optical cavity resonator to amplify the signal. Source energy is converted into optical energy through excitation of the atomic or molecular species in the active medium.

Optical *stimulated emission* is produced from the active material in which an inversion of the population of natural energy states has been contrived. The active material is bounded by reflecting surfaces between which the laser light is contained within a resonant cavity, in similar fashion to the microwave generator. The active element may be either a gas, a doped crystal, a semi-conductor or a liquid and the state of *population inversion* may be obtained by pumping, usually by means of electrical, optical or electron-beam methods. The laser output can be produced as either a continuous wave (CW), as a train of pulses (multiple pulse), or as a single giant pulse (Q-switching) of a few nanoseconds duration. These characteristics are discussed in more detail in the following sections.

Spontaneous Emission

In order to understand the differences between laser radiation and ordinary light, it is necessary to examine their different mechanisms of formation.

Ordinary light, as from an incandescent lamp, is emitted by excited atoms through the release of optical photons in the absence of an external stimulus. The process occurs at random and is called *spontaneous emission*. A photon is a packet or quantum of radiation which lasts for about 10^{-8} s for an isolated atom.

Figure 6.2 illustrates the sequence of events occurring in spontaneous emission. An atom in a lower energy state E_1 is raised to an excited state E_2 (*a*) by the absorption of a photon and, after staying in this state (*b*) for an arbitrary time, emits another photon (*c*) of energy $\Delta E = E_2 - E_1 = h\nu$ where ν is the photon frequency and h is Planck's constant. There is no amplification in this process and the radiation is said to be incoherent.

Stimulated Emission

The basic characteristics of laser radiation are its temporal coherence, giving it a high degree of monochromaticity, its spacial coherence, producing a high degree of directivity, and its very high source brightness. These qualities arise from the process of stimulated emission which is described below and illustrated in Figure 6.3.

It was shown by Einstein that if an atom or molecule is in a higher energy state the release of this stored energy can be controlled by subjecting the atom or molecule to an electromagnetic field of the same frequency. Comparison of Figure 6.3 with Figure 6.2 shows the essential difference between stimulated and spontaneous emission. For stimulated emission to occur the atom or molecule must

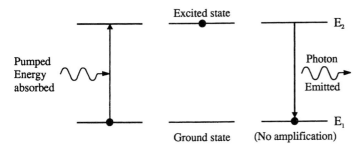

Figure 6.2 Spontaneous Emission

already be in an excited state E_2 before it absorbs a second photon and before it has time to decay by spontaneous emission. As a result, a second photon is emitted in the same direction and with the same frequency/wavelength and phase as the stimulating photon.

Coherence

The stimulated photon (Figure 6.3) is said to be *coherent* with the stimulating photon, i.e., the two photons are perfectly matched in phase and frequency. The result is to produce a gain of four in intensity which is twice that had they been out of phase with one another, as is the case for ordinary (incoherent) light. Further amplification in the cavity occurs as each photon creates more coherent photons by stimulated emission. In the ideal case the laser output wave is *spatially coherent*, resulting in perfect collimation, and *temporally coherent* resulting in perfect monochromaticity. Practical lasers do not achieve perfect coherence and the beam has a narrow bandwidth and a small divergence.

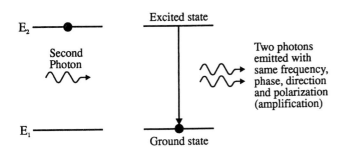

Figure 6.3 Stimulated Emission

Cavity Resonator and Population Inversion

For laser action to be sustained there must be a greater population of atoms in the higher energy state E_2 than in the lower energy state E_1. This is the opposite to the condition which occurs in the natural state of matter and is called *population inversion*. A cavity resonator is used to produce population inversion and also to amplify the wave. There is a close analogy with the microwave generator, the main difference being that there are many more competing oscillator modes in the optical cavity making a high degree of coherence more difficult to achieve. In its simplest form, Figure 6.4, it consists of an active medium between two plane mirrors, one of which is partially transparent to allow an external output in the form of a laser beam. Practical lasers use pairs of different types of mirror combination.

Pumping is achieved by external excitation which in the illustration is by DC or RF electrical discharge into a gas medium, but could be by other means. The pumping energy is used to raise atoms or molecules into the higher excited states and achieve a state of population inversion. Laser action is initiated by photons which are emitted spontaneously after pumping has commenced. These photons interact with the excited atoms as they pass through the cavity causing some of the atoms to de-excite by stimulated emission. Each photon produces a wave which grows in amplitude on successive interactions with the gas atoms and this wave is reflected back and forth by the cavity mirrors, stimulating more atoms and producing further amplification. If the gain by stimulated emission exceeds the losses, which occur, for example, by spontaneous emission, scattering and absorption in the active medium and by mirror reflection losses, the process of amplification continues. There is, of course, a deliberate loss through the partially reflecting mirror and good laser design is aimed at optimising the output coupling. If this is too high the loss rate may exceed the pumping rate and the oscillation ceases, and if too low there is not sufficient output power. Generally speaking, a mirror transmission of 1–10 per cent is usually employed. The efficiencies of most laser systems, measured as the ratio of the radiated coherent power to the pump power, lie in the range 0.05 per cent to 50 per cent, the remainder being dissipated in non-collectable energy by photons moving non-paraxially in the cavity and by the other processes mentioned above.

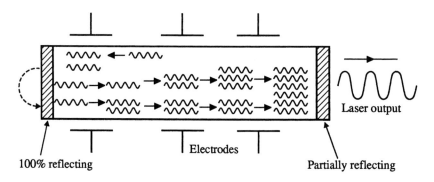

100% reflecting
Electrodes
Partially reflecting
Laser output

Figure 6.4 Concept of Cavity Resonator (showing, conceptually, the build-up of the amplified wave)

Types of Laser

Pumping Cycle of a Typical Laser

The pumping action in a practical laser is more complicated than the simple conceptual system described earlier and more than two atomic levels are always involved. The pumping oscillation cycle of a typical, solid-state laser system, e.g., Nd:YAG, which operates at four levels is shown in Figure 6.5.

In such a system the highest energy state E_4 is a broad absorption band of closely-spaced levels. These make an efficient reservoir for pump light of different frequencies (white light) to raise electrons from the ground state E_1. The excited atoms quickly decay to level E_3, followed by a laser transition to E_2 and subsequent further fast decay to the ground state E_1. This ensures that the lower laser transition state E_2 is emptied and the essential condition of population inversion is maintained throughout the lasing exposure. In a three-level system, e.g., ruby, there is no fast decay from E_2 to E_1, making population inversion more difficult to maintain, resulting in lower operational efficiency.

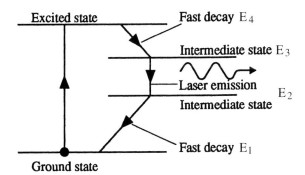

Figure 6.5 Pumping Cycle for a Four-Level Laser

Solid-State Lasers

Solid-state lasers offer the advantage, over gas lasers, of having a much higher volume density of ions and this makes for the smallest system and portability. Because they are so small and have low conversion efficiency, heat dissipation is a problem and limits their use for high average-power applications.

The principle of operation of the *ruby* and *neodymium* laser with an elliptical cavity is shown in Figure 6.6. Since pumping by atomic collisions is not possible in solids the laser material must be optically transparent to the radiation from the pumping source, which is a white light xenon flash tube. The flash tube is placed at one focus and the ruby or neodymium rod at the other.

The ruby crystal consists of aluminium oxide as the host material, to which has been added a small proportion of chromium in the form of triply-charged ions, as

113

the laser-active constituent. The ruby crystal suffers from low efficiency (0.05 per cent), causing heating at very low-pulse repetition frequency, which quenches the pumping action. It is necessary to cool the crystal to liquid nitrogen temperature in order to maintain a reasonable pumping speed and this adds to bulk.

Although the ruby laser is the original equipment for the *Chieftain* range finder, later service range finders use triply charged neodymium Nd^{3+} with yttrium aluminium garnate (YAG) as the host material. The laser output for the Nd:YAG laser is 1.06µm and its efficiency is about 2 per cent. The YAG host material has good thermal and optical properties and is capable of being operated at rates typically of 10–20 pulses per second, making it much more suitable than ruby for ranging and designating targets.

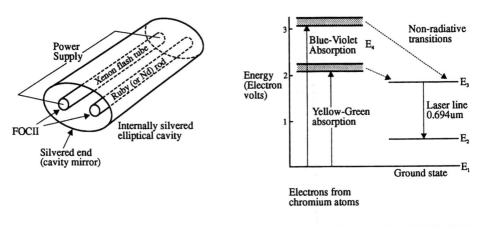

PHYSICAL ARRANGEMENT · · · · · · · MODE OF OPERATION, RUBY LASER

Figure 6.6 Principle of Operation of the Ruby (and Neodymium) Laser

Other types of optically pumped, solid-state laser which are being considered for military applications are based on *holmium* and *erbium* as the lasant materials. The host lattice for holmium may either be YAG or YLF (yttrium lithium fluoride) and operates at 2.06µm. The erbium YLF laser output is at 1.54µm. Both these laser wavelengths represent hazards to the cornea of the eye, not the retina, and consequently are safer. This advantage is offset by the fact that they are not as efficient as neodymium and more source energy is required to drive them.

The Raman-shifted Nd: YAG laser is a recent development. It makes use of the process of Raman scattering to change the wavelength from 1.06 to 1.54µm. Methane is normally used as the Raman medium because of its high conversion efficiency, typically 30 per cent. Like holmium and erbium, the Raman-shifted Nd:YAG laser offers the prospect of an eye-safe laser but it also retains neodymium technology and the high-pressure methane cell could be incorporated within the conventional Nd:YAG system.

The diode-pumped Nd:YAG laser employs a very narrow line-width diode laser to pump the Nd:YAG cavity during Q-switch operation (see below) to provide an intense, single-frequency output.

A recent development is the *alexandrite* laser. The host material is chrysoberyl, Al_2BeO_4, and the laser active dopant is the triply-charged chromium ion, Cr^{3+}. Broad emission bands give it the capability of wavelength tuning over the range 7 to 8.2µm.

The cavity oscillator of the solid-state laser is usually formed by silvering the ends of the laser rod or by using separate cavity mirrors. The output from such a simple resonator may have a mixture of transitions between various modes which can escape from the system and the resulting temporal shape is a series of spikes from these competing modes of oscillation. Careful design of the cavity can eliminate higher order modes, resulting in a gaussian-shaped beam profile and optimum output. In order to make this suitable for military applications the output pulse must be controlled, and for ranging systems has been achieved by a technique called Q-switching (see p 119) enabling very short pulses of high power to be produced.

Semi-Conductor Injection Lasers

These systems work on the principle of a p-n junction biased in the forward direction so that the positive holes are injected from the p-region towards the n-region and recombine with electrons in the junction to give up their energy as heat or light. Figure 6.7(a) illustrates this principle and Figure 6.7(b) the physical arrangement.

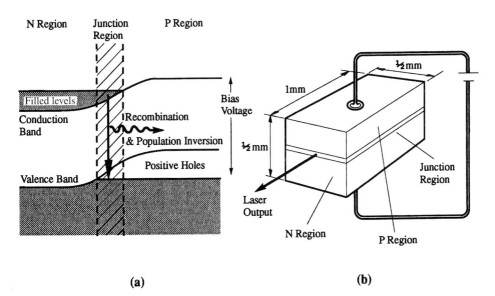

(a)   (b)

Figure 6.7 Semi-Conductor Laser

At high pumping current densities, near 5000 amps cm^{-2}, the p-n junction in *gallium arsenide* (GaAs) behaves as if it has a negative absorption coefficient for radiation so that when radiation passes through the junction region it is amplified; and if it is made in the form of an optical resonator the system becomes a laser. CW outputs of several milliwatts have been achieved at efficiencies up to 50 per cent in a wavelength band between 0.84 and 0.90μm. Modulation of the output provides the facility for ranging and communications.

The particular attractions of GaAs lasers are that they are highly efficient photodiodes of compact size and may be directly modulated by their drive current supply. They are, however, of low power and large beam divergence and thus have limited range-finding performance. Their main use is in fibre optics communication systems and they are also being developed for weapon-effects simulation applications.

Gas Lasers

Gas lasers are simple in construction and offer the greatest degree of versatility. They are capable of achieving a high degree of coherence and directionality and cover the widest range of output power. Optical pumping, such as is used for solid-state lasers, cannot be employed because there are no broad absorption bands; instead the mechanism is usually by electrical discharge to excite one type of atom which then transfers energy to the lasant atom by collision.

The *helium-neon* laser is a four-level system and was the first gas laser to be demonstrated. Pumping is achieved by direct-current or radio-frequency excitation of the helium atoms and this energy is transferred to the neon atoms by atomic collision. The neon atoms radiate by laser action principally at 0.63μm but other lines are emitted as well. The laser is designed to optimise for the lower order (TEM$_{oo}$) mode of operation but higher modes may appear if the mirrors are not accurately aligned. Beam quality is usually very good, i.e., approximates to a gaussian beam profile, but low gain restricts efficiency to less than 1 per cent.

The cavity is usually decoupled from the mirrors (Figure 6.8) to protect them from damage and the tube is sealed by a pair of anti-parallel optical flats set at the Brewster angle, thus polarising the laser output.

The *argon* laser operates on the basis of transitions between excited states of singly-ionised argon atoms which emit on several lines between 0.35 and 0.53μm. As it takes much more energy to ionise each atom, more input is needed for an argon laser as compared with a helium neon laser of the same output; thus water cooling is required adding bulk.

The principal gas laser of current interest to surveillance and target acquisition is the *carbon dioxide* laser. This works by molecular transitions in the carbon dioxide molecule which are closer together than atomic states and therefore a

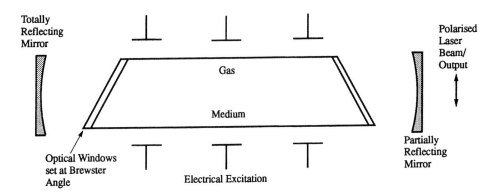

Figure 6.8 Helium Neon Laser

lower laser photon energy results, i.e., a longer photon wavelength is emitted. The carbon dioxide molecule emits in the range 9 to 11μm with the strongest line at 10.6μm, which is in the middle of the far infra-red atmospheric transmission window. Nitrogen and helium gas are also present. The nitrogen has a similar role to helium in a helium neon laser, that is, the nitrogen molecules are excited by an external pumping source and exchange energy with carbon dioxide molecules by collision. The helium assists population inversion by breaking down some of the non-productive levels in the carbon dioxide molecule.

The CO_2 laser is an adaptable system and there are several configurations. They range from small versions with a few milliwatts of continuous power to very high power devices of megawatts average power and of the order of 10 kilojoules pulse energy. They may achieve high efficiency typically of the order 30 per cent, and high beam quality.

The principal CO_2 laser for direct-detection (incoherent) range-finding operations is the transversely excited atmospheric (TEA) laser operating in pulsed mode. Peak output powers in the region of 200kW over a pulse length of 60 ns have been achieved with a cavity length of 0.25m and a repetition rate up to 100 Hz.

The pulsed CO_2 TEA laser is shown schematically in Figure 6.9. A uniform electric field is set up between two profiled electrodes and a trigger wire creates ultraviolet photon ionisation of the working gas. A homogeneous discharge is produced by the resulting electrons in the cavity. This action sets up the condition of population inversion and stimulated emission. Amplification is created by reflections from mirrors as with other laser cavities. The working gas is a mixture of CO_2, N_2 He, CO and H_2; the latter two gases are used to control the dissociation of CO_2 which occurs within the discharge volume. The trigger wire is controlled by pulse forming networks to give the desired pulse repetition rate profile.

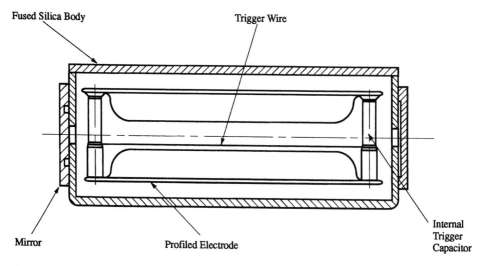

Figure 6.9 CO₂ TEA Laser

The CO_2 TEA laser is also used in the coherent detection, or heterodyne mode, of operation to measure target range and velocity, employing both pulsed and continuous-working laser types.

Another type of CO_2 laser is the high-pressure waveguide laser, so called because the excitation region is of a cylindrical shape small enough to guide the beam down the bore in a waveguide type of mode. The high working pressure results in a broadened line width (200 MHz) and allows for modulation formats involving much wider bandwidths. Though pulsed types have been developed, CW operation with electro-optic modulation is the most efficient mode. Operator-recognisable coherent imaging has been demonstrated by using Doppler techniques.

The CO_2 TEA laser exhibits good beam quality and is used with heterodyne detection, the principle of which is described below. This is the optical equivalent of microwave heterodyning and measures target range and velocity data. The heterodyne technique is complex but avoids some of the problems of sensitivity which are encountered in non-heterodyne detection and is probably less detectable because the emitted energy is lower.

Development in the use of the CO_2 laser for ranging applications is likely to be in the use of high repetition rates for combined ranging and target-designating purposes and deployed in conjunction with a thermal imager. Very compact, high-pressure waveguide-type lasers of the continuous output type are also being developed for communications.

Other relevant gas laser developments are the *chemical* and the *excimer* laser type. One chemical laser works on the basis of the combustion of fluorine with hydrogen or deuterium to produce emission at 2.5 and 3.8µm, respectively, the latter coming within the middle infra-red atmospheric transmission window. The excimer laser uses a mixture of rare gas and halogens to lase in the short visible and near ultraviolet. Examples are krypton fluoride emitting at 0.25μm and xenon chloride at 0.31μm. Efficiencies in excess of 10 per cent appear to be possible. Such lasers have applications in long-range space communications and short-range tactical surveillance operations.

Liquid Lasers

The most important liquid lasers from the military point of view are the fluorescent dyes such as the xanthene dye Rhodamine 6G which has hundreds of overlapping spectral lines, enabling it to be tuned between 0.7 and 1.0μm. It is possible, in principle, by using several dyes to achieve continuous tuning from the near ultra-violet through to the visible and near infra-red, offering even greater flexibility than the solid-state alexandrite laser in this respect.

Associated Techniques

Q-Switching

The method of Q-switching is employed with solid-state lasers to achieve very short, intense pulses of nearly monochromatic laser radiation for ranging and target designation applications.

Q-switching involves changing the 'quality' of the cavity. Initially the cavity mirrors are removed and pumping allows the population inversion to build up to a very high value of single-mode oscillation without the feedback which would have built up competing higher order mode oscillations. After the population inversion has achieved the highest possible value the mirrors are switched back into the system, suddenly increasing the Q-factor and feedback, allowing the whole of the stored energy to be emitted in one short, intense pulse, essentially of a single mode (TEM_{oo}) oscillation.

Q-switching can be done in several ways. In one technique an octagonal mirror, or porro-prism, is rotated at high speed, e.g., 30,000 rpm, and only when this is aligned with the stationary mirror is the energy released as laser output (Figure 6.10). This type of device produces pulses of width 50 ns and ranging accuracy of approximately 1m, but the switching speed is relatively slow.

A faster method employs an electro-optically generated switch, which is also shown in Figure 6.10. A Kerr cell contains nitrobenzene placed between a pair of electrodes. When an electric field is applied an optic axis is induced parallel to the direction of the field. Only along the optic axis is the refractive index independent of the direction of the polarisation of light. Plane-polarised light incident on the cell can, in general, be resolved into a component which vibrates parallel to the optic axis and a component which vibrates perpendicularly to it.

119

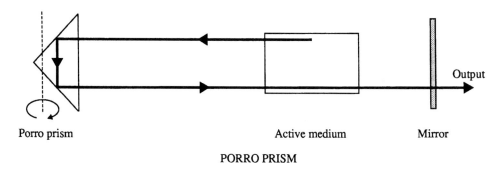

Porro prism   Active medium   Mirror

PORRO PRISM

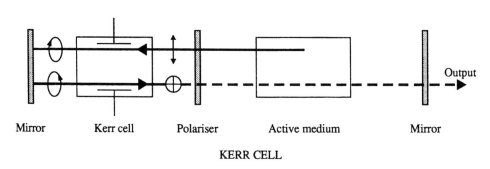

Mirror   Kerr cell   Polariser   Active medium   Mirror

KERR CELL

Figure 6.10 Two Types of Q-Switch

The velocities of the two components within the cell are different and upon emerging from the crystal are out of phase, generally producing an elliptically polarised output. If the angle of incidence of the incident plane polarisation is 45° to the optic axis and the phase difference is a multiple of $\pi/2$ the output is circularly polarised. In Figure 6.10 the cavity output light is made plane-polarised by the polariser and converted to circularly-polarised light by the Kerr cell. The cavity mirror reflects this polarised light and in doing so reverses the direction of polarisation. The light which re-emerges from the Kerr cell is also plane-polarised but at right angles to that transmitted by the polariser, thus it cannot be transmitted again by the polariser until the electric field is switched off. With the electric field on, the population inversion is allowed to increase and the mirrors are 'switched in' when the field is reduced to zero. The change in voltage must be synchronised with the pumping. With this technique output pulses of 10 ns can be produced, increasing ranging accuracy over the mechanical method.

For higher gains a saturable dye is introduced into the laser medium. Normally the dye strongly absorbs at the laser wavelength so that no amplification is possible. A point is reached in the build up of the population inversion when the gain due to stimulated emission exceeds the losses and laser action begins to take place. The dye becomes saturated by the optical flux and is rapidly switched into a state of transparency. The stored energy in the large population inversion is immediately emitted as an optical pulse in a few nanoseconds. The characteristics of the dye, e.g., its absorption cross-section and time constants, have to be carefully matched with the host material. This photochemical method is highly suitable for lightweighting applications.

Another method of controlling the output pulse is to use the technique of cavity dumping. Here the population inversion is allowed to build up to a peak value as in Q-switching, at which time an electro-optic switch is opened to allow the stored energy to be dumped into the cavity as optical radiation. Little or no radiation is allowed out of the cavity until the whole of the energy is converted, and at this time the switch opens a second channel so that all the optical energy is emitted in pulse times of the order of 1 ns. With these techniques ranging accuracies of about 0.1m can be achieved.

An even faster technique is called mode locking. The transmission of the electro-optic switch is modulated and synchronised to correspond with the photon round trip time in the cavity and enables pulses in the picosecond region to be produced.

Frequency Doubling

The technique of frequency doubling is to utilise an electro-optical process whereby incident laser beam energy is absorbed in a crystal and causes two photons at one wavelength to combine and produce a single photon at half that wavelength. In this way a Nd:YAG output at 1.06μm can be transformed into an emergent beam of 0.53μm.

Raman Wavelength Shifting

The Raman effect can be used to increase the wavelength of a laser beam by directing it into a suitable Raman active material. Practical energy conversion efficiencies can be achieved and the most obvious application is to shift the Nd:YAG wavelength of 1.06μm to 1.54μm, thereby substantially decreasing the eye hazard.

Adaptive Optics

Adaptive optics is an emerging technology which enables time-varying distortions in a laser beam to be automatically corrected. Its main application is in compensating for phase distortion produced by atmospheric turbulence, but it can also be used to correct for aberrations in the laser cavity resonator, i.e., restoring TEM_{oo} mode operation. Active corrections result in partial or total restoration of coherence and beam directivity and achievement of diffraction-limiting imaging performance.

There are two types of adaptive optics system. The earlier type is called the *multi-dither system* and operates in a manner similar to phased array radar. The system analyses the wave-fronts in the reflected returns from the target by a phase-sensitive detector and the data is used to make compensatory corrections to the phase of the outgoing laser beam wave-front. The beam director in this system consists of a two-dimensional set of small mirrors each of which makes small perturbations, called 'dithering', to effect the appropriate path difference correction pattern. Each is tagged by a characteristic frequency to locate these differences across the wave-front and to enable the associated phase error to be applied to the output wave. Simple surface-deformable mirrors have also been used but phased arrays are preferred, particularly for large area beam directors.

The second type of system makes use of non-linear optical phenomena. The functions of the phase-sensitive detectors, servo-mechanism and deformable mirrors of the multi-dither system are replaced by a *phase-conjugate* mirror. Essentially this mirror returns an incident laser beam back along the same path and with phase reversal. If the incident wave is distorted in phase the conjugator produces a return wave which is equally distorted but with phase reversed. Thus, when this wave passes back through the distorting medium, e.g., atmospheric turbulence, it cancels out the distortion and restores the coherence of the emerging beam. There are two kinds of phase-conjugate mirror, one which works on the basis of *simulated Brillouin scattering* and the other on a dynamic holographic process called *four wave mixing*, but the explanations of these complex phenomena are beyond the scope of this chapter. The important point from the military point of view is that the phase-conjugate mirror offers the prospect of high irradiance, coherent, self-targeted laser-beam propagation through the atmosphere and finds important applications in laser radar.

Laser Beam Propagation

TEM$_{00}$ Mode Propagation in Vacuum

A laser cavity resonator of the type used for target surveillance and acquisition may sustain several modes of oscillation or harmonics. Following microwave practice these are referred to as *transverse electro and magnetic (TEM$_{nm}$)*, the subscripts representing the number of interacting modes in orthogonal directions. These modes are present in the laser output beam and affect the beam quality, both in terms of wavelength, bandwidth and spatial characteristic.

The ideal condition is to limit the laser oscillation to the lowest harmonic, uniphase, basic mode, designated as TEM$_{00}$, because this would achieve the most monochromatic, highest intensity output, in the form of a gaussian circular profile. Higher order modes take a rectangular form, as illustrated in Figure 6.11, and a mixture of such modes produces structure in the laser output with reduction of intensity and consequent loss of performance.

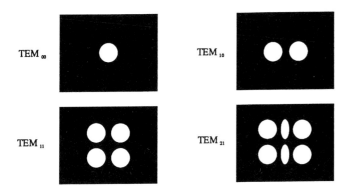

Figure 6.11 Transverse Electromagnetic (TEM) Modes

Only for the TEM_{00} mode is the laser output beam profile characterised unambiguously and it is convenient, for instructional purposes, to use the formula for this mode to give some idea of maximum range of effectiveness. Thus for TEM_{00} operation the diameter D of the laser beam as a function of range R (strictly in vacuum but, to a close approximation, applicable for clear atmospheric conditions) is given by the following expression:

$$D^2 = d^2 \left[1 + \left(\frac{4\lambda R}{\pi d^2} \right)^2 \right] \tag{1}$$

where λ is the wavelength of the laser radiation and d is the beam waist, which is taken as approximately 70 per cent of the diameter of the beam at the cavity exit. Table 6.2 shows how the beam diameter D varies with range R for a neodymium laser with different exit diameters d.

Table 6.2 Neodymium Laser Beam Diameter (m) as a Function of Range in Vacuum Assuming TEM_{00} Operation

Laser exit diameter d (m)	Range (m)			
	10	10^2	10^3	10^4
0.0002	0.006	0.06	0.6	6
0.02	0.02	0.02	0.06	0.60
0.1	0.10	0.10	0.10	0.12
0.2	0.20	0.20	0.20	0.20

The laser beam profile, as a graphical representation of Equation (1), is shown in Figure 6.12.

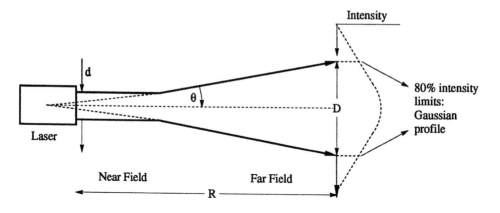

Figure 6.12 Laser Beam Profile for TEM$_{00}$ Mode of Oscillation

The features of Figure 6.12 are:

(i) a region in which the laser beam is essentially parallel, called the *near-field*, which covers ranges up to a maximum R_{NF} where

$$R_{NF} = \frac{\pi d^2}{4\lambda},$$

corresponding to that range where the first term in the bracket of Equation (1) is equal to the second term in the bracket;

(*ii*) a region in which the laser beam divergence is constant and equal to

$$\theta_{FF} = \frac{2\lambda}{\pi d},$$

called the *far-field* where the second term in the bracket of Equation (1) dominates; the far-field starts at approximately R_{NF}; for longer ranges than R_{NF} the beam diameter is, to a closer approximation as range increases, given by

$$D = \theta_{FF}R = \frac{2\lambda R}{\pi d}. \tag{2}$$

It is emphasised that the TEM$_{00}$ mode is a theoretical ideal which may not be met in practice. Production lasers can have higher order modes in their output, giving a broader beam divergence and may exhibit non-gaussian characteristics.

In many laser surveillance systems optics are inserted between the laser cavity and the exit aperture of the system, the purpose being to tailor the beam output to suit the particular application. One example of this use is to decrease the beam divergence of a multimode cavity output in order to increase range of effectiveness; Figure 6.18 illustrates this mode of operation. Another example is to expand the beam diameter of a TEM_{00} mode cavity output while also increasing beam divergence, thereby simplifying target aiming and tracking.

Atmospheric Effects

The main sources of intensity loss in passage through the atmosphere are:

- Through absorption and scattering by air molecules and aerosols which lie within the laser beam path. There are several types of aerosol such as water droplets which are encountered in haze, mist, fog, cloud and rain. In addition there are solid particulates such as dust, fumes and smokes. Absorption and scattering do not materially contribute to beam broadening.
- Through atmospheric turbulence, which produces temperature variations and variable refractive indices, causing intensity fluctuations, random partial focusing of the laser beam into 'hot-spots' called *scintillation* and additional beam broadening.
- For high-average-power focused laser beams the effect of molecular absorption is to cause heating of the local air which, if large enough, can produce intensity and refractive index gradients appropriate to a negative power distributed lens. The effect is to defocus the laser beam and the term 'thermal blooming' has been coined to describe this process. Thermal blooming can be reduced or eliminated by using pulsed beams and/or by slewing operations. This effect is not important for laser surveillance operations.

The transmission of visible and infra-red radiation through the atmosphere is an irregular and complex function of the wavelength, as is illustrated in Figure 6.13 typically for atmospheric visibilities of 5km and 20km. It can be seen that there are regions of high transmission, but also regions of strong absorption which are, principally, due to carbon dioxide molecules and water vapour.

It is, of course, the transmission 'windows' that are of practical value. These occur in the visible; in the near infra-red region, but with some molecular absorption bands between 0.9 and 2µm; in the middle infra-red region between 3 and 5µm, except for a large carbon dioxide absorption band at 4.3µm; and the whole of the far infra-red region between 8 and 14µm. This particular transmission spectrum relates to an actual coastal horizontal path and although the general

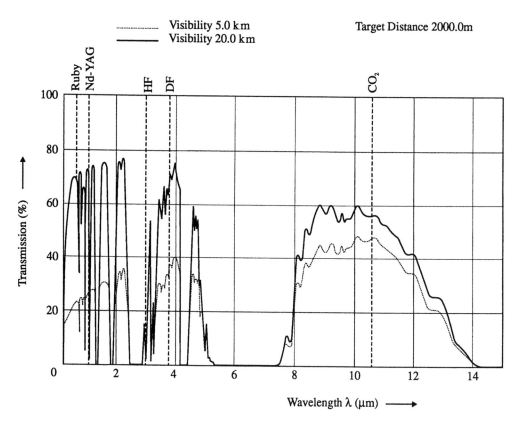

Figure 6.13 Atmospheric Transmission in the Optical Region

characteristics hold for other locations it may be expected that the presence of smokes and fumes will have an important effect; for example, in low-level battlefield operations. Diurnal variations associated with local terrain conditions may also be expected, making prediction difficult.

Generally it is aerosol scattering which dominates in the visible and the near infra-red region of the spectrum, whereas molecular absorption is the important intensity loss mechanism for the far infra-red. There is an order of magnitude increase in penetration through aerosols for CO_2 radiation over visible radiation for visibility ranges in excess of about 5km. Under such conditions the droplet sizes are probably less than 1μm. For fog conditions, however, where the droplet sizes increase up to about 50μm, the long wavelength advantage in aerosol penetration is lost.

Table 6.3 gives an indication of the sizes of some of the important atmospheric constituents. It is to be expected from this data that the increased range effectiveness of the middle and the far infra-red band would hold for dusts and smokes, as well as haze but not for heavy fumes and fogs.

Table 6.3 Aerosol Sizes (μm)

smokes	0.2–2
dust	1–10
fumes	up to 100
haze	up to 1
fog and cloud	5 to 50
mist	50 to 100
drizzle	100 to 500
rain	500 to 5000

Atmospheric turbulence causes scintillation, beam broadening and wander to an amount which depends upon the range, the degree of turbulence and the wavelength of the laser radiation. Typically, high turbulence could produce an order of magnitude increase in focused beam diameter at 5μm, thus decreasing intensity by two orders of magnitude.

Because molecular absorption is stronger at the longer wavelength, it is expected that thermal blooming is the intensity limiting feature for high power propagation, whereas in the visible and the near infra-red region turbulence induced beam spreading and aerosol scattering are the limiting propagation effects. The middle infra-red region appears to offer the best compromise for high power propagation, though the actual physical and atmospheric conditions will determine the optimum wavelength.

Laser Radar (LADAR)

Introduction
There are two types of LADAR. The first is called the *direct detection* mode or technique in which the laser is employed as a very bright source and is an extension of the lower performance LIDAR (Light Detection And Ranging) technique which uses ordinary, incoherent, light sources such as xenon and other flash lamps. Most of the applications in target ranging and designating make use of this method.

The second type makes full use of the temporal and spatial coherence of the laser beam and is the optical equivalent of RADAR. It uses *heterodyne detection* in the manner of the microwave method to achieve two orders of magnitude lower noise in the optical receiver compared with the direct detection technique, but at the expense of system complexity.

LADAR Equation

The general LADAR equation for a *solid* target has the following form:

$$P_r = \left(\frac{P_1}{R^2 \, \Omega_1} \right) \cdot (\rho A_t) \cdot \left(\frac{A_c}{R^2 \Omega_r} \right) T^2 \qquad (3)$$

where
P_r = return signal power,
P_1 = laser transmitted power,
Ω_1 = laser beam divergence solid angle,
Ω_r = target scattered beam solid angle,
ρ = target reflectance,
A_t = target area,
A_c = receiver area,
R = range, and
T = one-way propagation path transmittance.

When the entire scattered target beamwidth is intercepted by the receiver aperture the equation becomes:

$$P_r = \left(\frac{P_1}{R^2} \right) \left(\frac{\rho A_t}{\Omega_r} \right) T^2 \qquad (4)$$

Equation (3) is applicable in general for non-co-operative targets where the scattered beam from a diffuse, e.g., Lambertian, reflector is scattered over a wide angle. Equation (4) relates particularly to co-operative targets where retroreflection techniques are used to contain the return signal in a very narrow beam. The LADAR return from co-operative targets may be many orders of magnitude greater than from non-co-operative ones.

In the transition region between these two extremes the return signal strength depends upon the shape of the transmitted beam and the back-scatter pattern of the target. In the absence of beam jitter, the return power in this region varies as the inverse cube of the range; but with beam jitter only statistical fractions of the laser beam hit the target and return power computation becomes more difficult.

In the presence of laser-induced target emissions the same general Equation (3) applies but the appropriate emission cross-section is used in place of the target reflectance. In this case it is assumed that spectral discrimination in the receiver is available.

For solid targets the quantity

$$\frac{\rho A_t}{\Omega_r}$$

is called the LADAR cross-section, in analogy with the RADAR cross-section. The average returned power is usually expressed in terms of the former and is important because it determines the signal-to-noise ratio in the receiver.

The return signal strength must be greater than a minimum value, which is determined by the noise characteristics of the receiver detector. The signal-to-noise ratio, S/N, is related to these characteristics and to the return signal strength by the following equation:

$$S/N \ = \ \frac{P_r}{[(NEP)^2 \times 4/\tau]^{\frac{1}{2}}} \tag{5}$$

where NEP is the noise equivalent power of the detector and τ is the pulse width.

By way of example to illustrate these features: if $P_1 = 1$ megawatt, $\tau = 40$ nanosec, the receiver aperture diameter is 0.05m and the wavelength is 1.06μm (neodymium), the return signal from a target of reflectivity 0.01 at a range of 1km is approximately 5×10^{-6} watts, making due allowance for atmospheric losses over the outward and return paths. For an assumed NEP of 10^{-10} watts $(Hz)^{-1}$ the signal to noise ratio S/N would be about 5 to 1 and the target could easily be ranged.

In the case of a *distributed gaseous* or vapour target, e.g., a chemical agent, the reflectance is of a more tenuous nature, being a function of distance into the target. It is conventional to define a volume backscatter coefficient $\beta(R)$ (units of $m^{-1} sr^{-1}$) where R is the range of the target from the receiver. The main contribution to the return signal arises from elastic scattering from aerosols of size comparable with the wavelength of the radiation and is known as Mie scattering. Mie scattering is strong in the infra-red and enables very small concentrations of aerosols to be detected. Rayleigh scattering by air molecules is weak in comparison. Additionally there might be fluorescent and Raman scattering returns.

A form of the LADAR equation for a *gaseous* target is:

$$P_r \ = \ P_1 \Delta R \cdot \beta(R) \ \frac{A_c}{R^2} \ T^2. \tag{6}$$

ΔR corresponds to the time-resolved range interval at range R.

129

$$\Delta R = \frac{C\tau}{2}, \qquad (7)$$

where τ = pulse length.

Equations (6) and (3) are dimensionally compatible in the sense that $\Delta R\,\beta(R)$ has units of sr^{-1} and corresponds with the reciprocal of Ω_r.

T, the atmospheric transmission, factor may be written:

$$T = \int_0^R e^{-\mu(r)dr}. \qquad (8)$$

μ is called the attenuation (or extinction) coefficient and is a measure of the loss in intensity by the laser radiation as it traverses along the beam path. This loss arises because of absorption and scattering by the molecules and aerosols in the atmosphere. For a condition of pure Rayleigh elastic scattering which corresponds to clear air situations, $\mu \simeq 4\pi\beta$, and although this simple relationship does not exactly hold for aerosol scattering the β/μ relationship is similar.

Figure 6.14 is a plot of P_r/P_1 versus range R for values of β for a system with $A_c = 0.1m^2$ and $\Delta R = 5m$.

The atmosphere itself will have a β coefficient depending upon the conditions

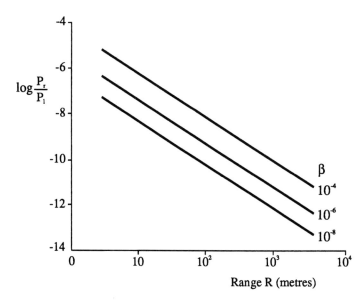

Figure 6.14 P_r/P_1 Plot Versus Range (R) for Different β

and sets a lower limit to the concentration of chemical agent which can be detected. Some typical values for β are shown in Table 6.4.

Table 6.4 Atmospheric β Coefficients

Atmospheric conditions	β (m^{-1} sr^{-1})
clear	1×10^{-6}
haze	2×10^{-6}
clouds	8×10^{-6}
fog	2×10^{-4}

Most LADAR studies of gaseous concentrations have used visible or near infra-red lasers because of the high aerosol scatter at these wavelengths, i.e., β is larger. Carbon dioxide laser beams would suffer much less attenuation in hazy and smoky conditions, i.e., μ is smaller, and have been used extensively in pollution studies because they are absorbed by a variety of atmospheric and pollutant molecules, being the basis of the differential absorption (DIAL) technique referred to in the section on laser radar spectroscopy. Detailed analysis is beyond the scope of this chapter, but minimum detectable concentrations of the technique typically are one part in 10^8.

Comparison with Microwave RADAR

Equation (1) applies for all wavelengths, from which it may be deduced that the region over which the TEM_{oo} beam is highly collimated, i.e., the near field, is some 10^4 times greater for an optical laser compared with a microwave generator of the same cavity diameter. A microwave generator operating at 0.01 m wavelength would require a 5m diameter transmitter to produce the same range of beam parallelism as a neodymium laser with a cavity diameter of only 0.05m. More significantly, the laser beam far-field divergence beyond this range limit would be one hundred times smaller than that of the microwave generator. The energy of the laser beam is thus concentrated in a much smaller area and this high directionality gives the beam the potential for operation over much longer distances (particularly in the vacuum of space) than a microwave generator of the same power, though adverse weather does reduce this propagation advantage at low altitude.

Additional advantages of LADAR over RADAR for some applications are the ability to achieve extremely narrow beam-widths without significant side-lobes, greatly improving covertness and resistance to jamming. The high levels of spatial and angular resolution which can be obtained greatly improve target profiling definition, signature and tracking precision. The virtual absence of side-lobes also enables low-elevation tracking without clutter or multi-path effects. A much higher target range and radial velocity precision can be achieved by using laser heterodyning, utilising the coherent characteristic of the laser beam. The amount of signal processing required in the optical technique is high but there is a large information bandwidth available and this enables high data rates to be utilised.

A unique feature of the laser beam, particularly in the near ultraviolet, is that the frequency could be sufficiently high to excite electronic levels in the target material and subsequent de-excitation through fluorescence emission; or Raman scattering can, in principle, add to the return signal; both techniques improve target signature analysis and recognition.

Technical disadvantages of LADAR relative to RADAR are, arguably, lower coherence and lower source efficiency. Solid-state lasers have relatively poor spectral purity which makes them unsuitable for phase utilisation, but gas lasers have good temporal and spatial coherence making them suitable for use of phase in signal processing. Gas lasers also have the highest working efficiency, achieving in excess of 10 per cent in carefully designed systems.

The most important disadvantage of LADAR relative to RADAR is the more severe laser-beam intensity losses in propagation, especially through the lower

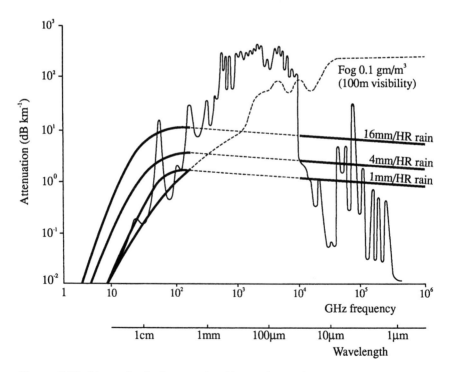

Figure 6.15 Atmospheric Attenuation Versus Operating Frequency

atmosphere. This is much less troublesome as the altitude increases and has no deleterious effect in the exoatmosphere, giving much scope for LADAR applications in ground-to-space and space-to-space environments. Figure 6.15 compares the attenuation for horizontal paths at sea level of these electromagnetic radiations under different conditions.

Both techniques use basically the same equation to determine the strength of the return signal from the target, the main difference being that the target properties are different. Target RADAR cross-sections have been better defined than the equivalent LADAR ones but the gap is closing. See also Figure 6.16 to appreciate the higher Doppler shift sensitivity in the optical band.

Laser Doppler Heterodyning

Doppler LADAR is used for target ranging and recognition; the principle of operation is described below.

The frequency of backscattered radiation from a target moving with velocity V at an angle θ towards or away from the transmitter is increased or decreased by an amount f_d where

$$f_d = \frac{2V f_0 \cos \theta}{c} \qquad (9)$$

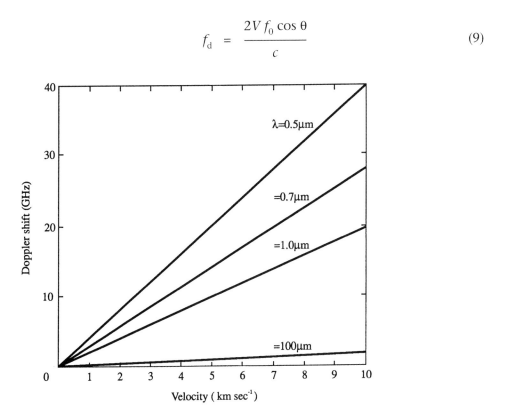

Figure 6.16 Doppler Shift as a Function of Target Velocity for Different Laser Wavelengths

133

and f_0 is the frequency of the transmitter and c is the velocity of the laser radiation.

Figure 6.16 is a plot of this equation for several wavelengths and target velocities. It clearly shows the increased sensitivity at the visible and near infra-red wavelengths.

This technique is illustrated in Figure 6.17 and described below.

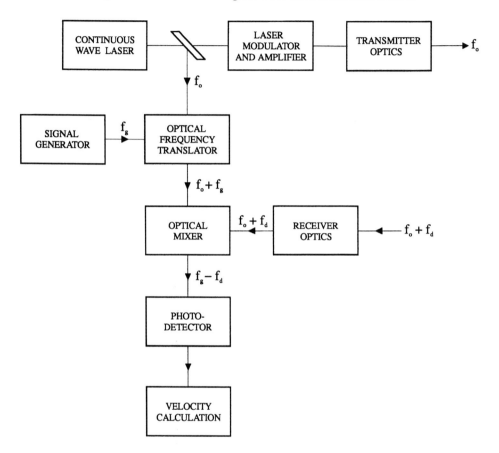

Figure 6.17 Doppler System

The laser signal of frequency f_o is modulated and amplified before transmission to the moving target, which returns the energy shifted by the Doppler frequency f_d. As this frequency normally would be too high to be handled by the photodetector, a reference frequency f_g is first combined with a local oscillator signal and the sum $|f_o + f_g|$ then mixed with the return signal to produce a frequency difference $|f_g - f_d|$ which is fed to the photodetector. Since f_g is known, the Doppler frequency f_d is determined by measuring $|f_g - f_d|$. The radial velocity may then be deduced from Equation (9) and the target range obtained from the time difference between the transmitted and the return signal.

The pre-detection portion of the heterodyne receiver is much more complex than that of the receiver in the direct (incoherent) technique. This is brought about as a consequence of the local oscillator, and the stability of alignment of the beam splitters and mirrors supplying the local oscillator at the detector are critical. Following radar heterodyne practice, a filter bank in the post-detection circuitry is matched to the transmitted waveform, each component of the filter being matched to a different Doppler-shifted version of this waveform.

The predominant source of noise in the heterodyne receiver is shot noise generated by the local oscillator and dominates strongly over external noise and dark current. This may be minimised by ensuring that the power of the local oscillator greatly exceeds the signal power, by making the active area of the photomixer as small as possible and by cooling the photomixer and its load resistor. Local oscillator powers of a few milliwatts are usually adequate. Techniques such as modulation and phase-sensitive detection, or integration over substantial time periods with narrow-band electronics (lock-in amplifiers) can be used to reduce bandwidths and increase signal-to-noise ratio.

Classical radar performance curves may be applied to the optical heterodyne case, the equivalent signal to noise ratio, S/N, in decibels for the LADAR mode being stated as:

$$10 \log_{10} \left(\frac{S}{N} \right) = 10 \log_{10} \left(\frac{\eta E}{hf} \right) \tag{10}$$

where η = quantum efficiency of the photo-surface of the detector; E = incident energy on to the detector; f is the mean frequency of the radiation on to the photodetector, and h is Planck's constant.

Laser Radar Spectroscopy

There are several types of laser radar spectroscopy. Differential absorption LIDAR (DIAL) is the most well developed. It employs two pulses at different wavelengths, one of which is absorbed strongly by the atmospheric species of interest, e.g., a chemical agent, and the other measures the background signal; thus the differential measures the concentration. A similar technique, called differential scattering (DISC), measures the difference in scattered intensity between the two laser beams from which the concentration can be deduced. In both cases range profiles may be obtained by measuring the signal returns as a function of time.

Raman LADAR is based upon the process of Raman scattering which occurs when the scattered laser light is shifted in wavelength with respect to the incident light. The Raman shift is equal to the vibrational frequency of the relevant molecule and the Raman intensity is directly proportional to the number density. A vast increase in sensitivity can be achieved by matching the incident wavelength exactly with the vibrational level of the species of interest; this technique is called resonance Raman LADAR.

Fluorescence LADAR is based upon the detecting of the laser induced fluorescence from the species of interest and is an extension of the Raman resonance scattering technique. For maximum effect the laser wavelength must correspond to the peak of an absorption line in the interacting molecule and as such peaks are more prolific at shorter wavelengths a tuned near ultra-violet laser gives the best performance.

The potential of these techniques does not yet appear to have been exploited in the military surveillance field.

APPLICATIONS TO SURVEILLANCE AND TARGET ACQUISITION

Introduction

The increasing use of lasers as part of surveillance systems reflects the unique characteristics these devices offer for accurate targeting with increased covertness, having particular advantages over radar for glancing angle, low-level attack by air.

The principal lasers for these operations are Nd:YAG operating at 1.06µm, CO_2 working at 10.6µm, and GaAs at 0.8–0.9µm; but lasers at other wavelengths may be deployed and the emergence of Raman-shifted Nd:YAG to 1.54µm results in an eye-safe laser without any compromising of its performance.

It is difficult to generalise on the laser beam characteristic and performance levels required because these depend upon the particular application. Likewise, to recommend whether pulsed or continuous-wave laser profiles should be employed, though pulsed systems tend to be simpler and thus perhaps more reliable and less expensive.

In general terms, for rangefinding against ground targets a pulse power (product of pulse energy and pulse width) of about 1 megawatt and a pulse repetition rate of the order 10 Hz is usually required. For fast moving air targets and for target designating the pulse power requirement is a factor five greater and the repetition rate is some two to three times higher. For guidance and tracking of air targets the pulse rate could be up to a few hundred hertz depending upon the particular scenario.

Rangefinding
The laser rangefinder has significantly improved first strike operations and versions have been developed for a wide range of scenarios.

In operation, the laser rangefinder emits an intense, highly collimated beam of short pulses which are reflected from the target back to the receiver. The time taken for a single pulse to travel out to the target and return is measured and converted into a direct reading of range.

The advantage of the laser in this operation is the achievement of high peak power output combined with narrow pulse width and low beam divergence to give long range of detection and good range resolution. Most of the laser rangefinders in operation use either Q-switched solid-state lasers or CO_2 TEA lasers achieving a range resolution of typically ±5m up to ranges of 20km.

Figure 6.18 shows the layout of a typical solid-state laser rangefinder. The laser output is coupled to a small transmitting telescope which decreases the transmit beam divergence and hence increases potential operational range. Part of this output is fed to a photodiode which provides the start pulse for a range counter. The laser beam is reflected by the target and some of the energy is collected by a receiver lens and focused on to the detector. The detector is protected by a narrow band interference filter which passes only the wanted signal and hence reduces background noise. The detector output is amplified and, if above an acceptable threshold level, is used to stop the range counter. The number of

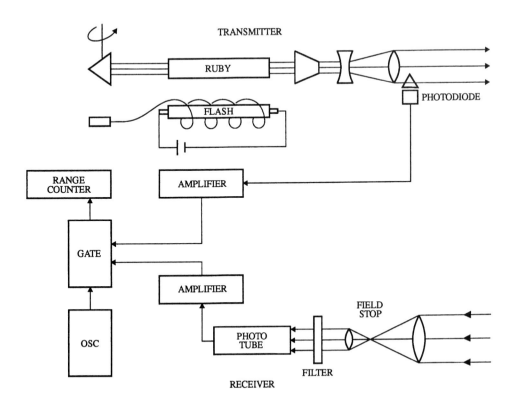

Figure 6.18 Layout of Pulsed Solid State Laser Rangefinder

pulses in the range display is a measure of the range and this is converted into a direct readout display.

In practice, for example, target engagement by a Main Battle Tank, the rangefinder is aligned to the axis of the tank's main gun and the sight is laid onto the target by the gunner using a ballistic graticule. The range of the target is presented to the gunner in the eye piece and this information is used to elevate the sight and gun axis until an aiming mark, selected according to the type and range of ammunition in use, is aligned onto the target. The tank gun is then set to produce the correct ballistic trajectory to the target. In some versions, the sight is coupled on line to a computer for direct fire control applications. In this mode the computer controls a cathode ray which is used as an aiming mark and is presented into the gunner's sighting system, or it can be used with a thermal imager to provide the gunner with a capability of ranging at night or in poor visibility. Most rangefinders are multiple pulsed, typically with repetition rates of 10 Hz, giving the capability of rejecting spurious signals from trees and smokes, for example, by using two range counters combined with 'first-last' switching selection, thus allowing the true target echo to be recorded.

Equipments are in service for rangefinding prior to engagement with indirect fire weapons or as an integral part of direct fire weapons.

An early laser rangefinder is the Barr and Stroud, Type LF2, which was fitted to the Chieftain tank. This system is based upon a ruby laser working at 0.69μm and is a single shot device. Ruby is a three-level laser and has been replaced by the more efficient four-level multi-shot Nd:YAG laser operating at 1.06μm which is less hazardous to the eye than ruby and, being invisible, has the advantage of extra covertness. Nd:YAG is now widely used for target rangefinding and designating operations.

The GEC-Marconi Type 520 laser rangefinder is the Nd:YAG replacement for Chieftain and is also in service with other armoured fighting vehicles. The same company produces the Type 105 laser rangefinders designed for air-to-surface operations, again based upon Nd:YAG at 1.06μm and offers different options for beam steering. This system operates up to a maximum range of 10km and an angular coverage of ±10°. It is in operational service with Draken aircraft of the Royal Danish Air Force and the British Aerospace Hawk 100.

The carbon dioxide CO_2 laser, operating at 10.6μm wavelength, has advantages over the ruby and neodymium lasers for rangefinding operations. In the operational context it has increased penetration in adverse atmospheric conditions, such as haze and mist, whenever the visibility is less than 5km and it also has superior penetration of battlefield smokes, thus enabling the target to be ranged at greater distances in poor conditions.

Another advantage of CO_2 is that it is optically compatible with thermal imagers working in the far infra-red band enabling, through co-operative action with common optics, target recognition and range to be established simultaneously over a 24 hour period.

A further advantage of CO_2 is that the Maximum Permissible Exposure (MPE) (see page 153 for definition) for CO_2 lasers is some three orders of magnitude greater than for Nd:YAG and four orders of magnitude greater than for ruby. This substantial relaxation in hazard to the naked eye enables restrictions placed upon personnel in training exercises to be much reduced or even dispensed with. Furthermore, as glass is opaque to 10.6μm the operators' eyes in conventional direct viewing systems, i.e., binoculars, are protected by the front optic, in contrast to the situation for Nd:YAG where a very high degree of convergence onto the highly sensitive retina would result.

By way of example, a CO_2 laser rangefinder operating single shot with a 50 ns pulse and a 0.05m diameter germanium lens aperture does not exceed the MPE for corneal damage even at zero range for peak power outputs less than 5 MW which is considered ample for ranging operations. A CO_2 continuous wave laser with a 0.05m diameter optic can operate up to 2 watts output before exceeding the corneal damage threshold and this is also an ample power for ranging applications. These lasers are designated Class I, and, as such are unequivocally eye safe, in contrast to ruby and neodymium.

Carbon dioxide lasers can also be operated in a number of modes including CW, modulated CW and repetitively pulsed. Frequencies up to 1 kHz can be achieved and optical heterodyne detection techniques can be employed enabling the superior temporal and spatial coherence properties of the CO_2 laser beam to be fully exploited, utilising the pure LADAR technique but at the expense of increased technical complexity.

The Type 116 CO_2 laser rangefinder has been developed by GEC-Marconi. This is based upon the Transversely Excited Atmospheric (TEA) laser producing a peak pulse power of 250kW, a pulse energy nominally of 30 mJ and beam divergence of 0.5 mrad. The system was developed initially for airborne applications and weighs 18.5kg. It has a ranging capability from 0.2 to 10km.

GEC-Marconi has also developed a tank laser sight Type 307 producing in excess of 500kW pulse peak power from a CO_2 TEA laser out to 5km range.

Photographs of both these instruments are shown in Figure 6.19.

The search for eye-safe laser rangefinders in the near infra-red is evolving in the form of Raman-shifted Nd:YAG at 1.54μm and in the use of diode lasers operating in the wavelength range 0.8 to 0.9μm (near term) and 1.54μm (long term). Examples of Raman-shifted lasers are the recently produced variant of the standard 1.06μm GEC-Marconi LRMTS; and Carl Zeiss HALEM 11 (hand-held) and MOLEM (mounted). Carl Zeiss are also developing a diode laser rangefinder for ranges up to 2000m which can be either hand held or incorporated into a target locator system.

(a)   (b)

Figure 6.19 CO2 Laser Rangefinders (a) GEC-Marconi Type 116 (b) GEC-Marconi Tank Laser Sight Type 307 *(photos by courtesy of GEC-Marconi Avionics Ltd)*

Target Designation

The use of laser equipments is improving the effectiveness of close air support and of artillery. The principle of target designation is that the target is illuminated by a laser beam and a detector in the aircraft nose or artillery shell (so-called 'smart munition') homes in on the reflected light from the target. The laser's narrow beam ensures very accurate, selective, marking accuracy at ranges up to about 10km and reduces the chances of detection by the enemy. Coded modulation increases covertness and removes ambiguity from the target return. The designator can be operated by a soldier on the ground or it can be carried in a co-operative aircraft. The laser has great advantages over conventional radar in being able to provide very accurate ranging rate data at the shallow angles which are encountered in low-level air attack of ground targets.

The complete system developed for British forces contains a Laser Target Marker and Ranger (LTMR) operated by a Forward Air Controller (FAC); and a compatible set of equipment in the aircraft, known as a Laser Ranger and Marked Target Seeker (LRMTS). The concept is illustrated in Figure 6.20.

The principle of operation is that as the aircraft approaches the target the LTMR is switched on by the FAC and emits a stream of laser pulses which strike the target. Some of the reflected energy is detected by a quadrant detector in the LRMTS which activates gimbal servo-motors to bring the sighting optic axis in line with the target and gives the pilot directional information enabling him to acquire and track the target automatically. The pilot flies the aircraft so that an

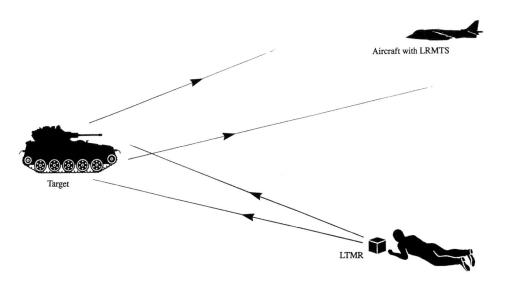

Figure 6.20 Target Designator Concept

aiming mark presented in his head-up display aligns with the target. Once the system has locked onto the target the LRMTS rangefinder takes over from the LTMR and gives the pilot a continuous update of the range to target. The pilot's task is then to use the ranging information and target datum in his head-up display to fly the aircraft and effect precise and automatic weapon release.

If no LTMR is available the airborne equipment can be used in the acquisition mode but the pilot's task is made more difficult as he first has to locate the target and then aim the laser.

The LTMR can be used for a range of equipments which are being developed for homing onto laser illuminated targets from ground and helicopter platforms and is photographed in Figure 6.21(a). This figure refers to the GEC-Marconi Type 306 target designator, which is based on the Nd:YAG laser. It has a pulse energy of 80 mJ and a beam divergence of 0.25 mrad. Ranging performance is up to 10km.

A GEC-Marconi LRMTS is in service with Jaguar, Harrier and Tornado (Figure 6.21b). It is based upon a Q-switched Nd:YAG laser and is compatible with all current NATO designators when used in co-operative mode. It is optimised for low level, first pass attack at grazing angles against difficult targets by minimising tracking time and has greatly improved weapon accuracy of ground attack aircraft. The laser cavity is folded for compactness and high optical stability, and the output is injected into a transmitter telescope. A silicon avalanche photodiode is used for ranging and a quadrant detector for position control. The laser beam is fully stabilised against aircraft movements by mounting the transmit and receive optics within a three-axis gimbal head which is used to direct the laser beam in elevation and azimuth.

Figure 6.21 (a) Laser Target Marker and Range Type 306 *(photo courtesy of GEC-Marconi Avionics Ltd)*

Figure 6.21 (b) Laser Ranger and Marked Target Seeker in the Harrier *(photo courtesy of GEC-Marconi Avionics Ltd)*

A 'Raman-shifted' version of LRMTS is now available. This converts the 1.06μm Nd:YAG laser output to a wavelength of 1.54μm, thereby achieving a virtually eye-safe system for training operations without compromising performance. The converter cell can be bolted on to the standard production LRMTS unit and no modifications to designator or aircraft are required.

Another important target designator system which has been developed by GEC-Marconi is called TIALD, an acronym for Thermal Imaging and Airborne Laser Designator. The TIALD pod can be fitted under the fuselage or wing positions on Jaguar, Harrier and Tornado aircraft and is intended for the accurate delivery of laser guided munitions either in self-designating mode or in co-operative action with other aircraft carrying the munitions. It has been used successfully in operational scenarios.

In operation TIALD is directed on to the target area as the aircraft makes its final approach. Once the target has been selected, the system locks on to the signal provided by the thermal imager or the TV video which is presented in a 'head-down' display together with the aircraft's flight symbology, enabling the aircraft to manoeuvre without losing target lock. At this time the laser may be fired to acquire target range and bearing through the aircraft's computer, which also provides data for the tracking algorithm by updating this information. The TIALD pod system is a self-contained unit powered from the aircraft and interfacing with the avionics. The main components are illustrated in Figure 6.22. The forward section contains the dual field of view, far infra-red thermal imager and optional TV unit for target acquisition and recognition; also the laser designator, relay optics and stabilised mirror system. The pod also contains video auto-tracking, sightline software control and stabilisation technologies allowing a

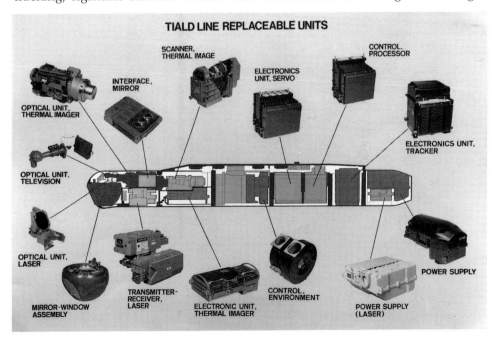

Figure 6.22 TIALD Pod System *(photo courtesy of GEC-Marconi Avionics Ltd)*

wide field of regard to be covered while achieving a high degree of harmonisation between acquisition (TI or TV) and laser sightlines. The latter are directed to the target area either by commands from the aircraft avionics using preplanned target co-ordinate information from the aircraft's navigation system or through manual joystick control by the aircrew.

Other designators developed by GEC-Marconi are the Type 306 LTMR (shown in Figure 6.21a) for ground and helicopter-mounted designating, and the Type 905 Designator for naval applications. Another naval General Purpose Electro-Optical Designator (GPEOD) developed by Ericsson is also in service. All three designators operate at 1.06μm but could have the Raman-shifted option.

An American equivalent of TIALD is the Martin Marietta LANTIRN laser targeting pod. Martin Marietta has also developed a laser-guided artillery shell called *Copperhead* which is designed to destroy an armoured vehicle with one or two shots. *Copperhead* has a laser detector in its nose and the internal equipment has to survive very high linear and rotational acceleration and high temperature when the gun is fired.

Target Illumination

The Army's requirement to enhance its night vision capability has led to the use of lasers to improve the performance of image intensifiers. In its simplest form such a device consists of a small torch which is used to illuminate the target when the ambient light conditions are unfavourable for the image intensifier acting alone. One such device uses a gallium arsenide laser in the continuous wave mode, having an output power of 100mW and giving a spot diameter which can be varied between 1.5 and 8m at 100m range.

More sophisticated systems have been developed which use gated viewing of the target. This technique considerably reduces the effect of atmospheric back-scatter which is the main cause of contrast degradation in conventional illumination of the target by incoherent, near infra-red radiation. With a pulsed laser, the receiver needs to be switched on for only a short time after each pulse is emitted and the effect of backscatter is thus greatly reduced. Viewing may be either direct by image intensifier or indirect by incorporating a television camera. The latter method is known as low-light television (LLTV).

Target Identification

The techniques of laser radar spectroscopy might be used to identify targets in specific cases where the signature is previously known.

Laser Doppler heterodyning may be used for active target imaging and vibration sensing. In the imaging mode the use of range-gating, velocity-gating and gating of the return signal intensity enhances target-to-background contrast. Employment of colour coding gives further target information, such as different textures and the relative movement of components, such as aerials and turrets. In the vibration mode the target is identified by its characteristic vibration signature which may be a function of its activity state.

Target Tracking

Lasers are most suitable for tracking targets, particularly for low-level and night-time operations. The laser rangefinder is often part of the tracking system, but dedicated heterodyne laser trackers may also be used in similar operation to microwave counterparts.

There is a wide range of tracking scenarios, each one placing a different emphasis on the system. For example, the requirements for tracking a satellite are not the same as those for tracking a missile or aircraft because the angular rates are vastly different; in this latter group there are different requirements for hostile and co-operative targets. In almost all cases, however, probably there will be a need for a conventional radar or passive optical viewer, and of wide field-of-view to acquire the target or targets, before handing over to the more accurate, but narrower field-of-view optical tracker. The analogy in astronomy is the use of a wide-angle telescope to locate a stellar object, then changing to a high-power, narrow-angle telescope to study its details.

The advantages of a laser tracker are: small system size, cheapness, very short pulses, direct modulation of the laser cavity and high modulation frequencies because the carrier wave frequency is high. High spectral brightness coupled with high collimation makes it suitable for covert, long-distance tracking in clear environments with high stray-light background rejection. The short wavelength makes for a practical size for the retroreflection from co-operative targets. Its directionality makes it less susceptible to countermeasures and lack of side-lobes makes it insensitive to the multiple-path effects that affect radar. Mutual interference between laser beams is not a problem, hence incomplete spectral coverage does not have the same importance as in the microwave region.

The disadvantages are that lasers are very sensitive to weathering effects, particularly those which operate in the visible and the near infra-red band, and the problem of eye damage is more acute in this spectral region. Pulsed lasers are subject to photon noise effects which are not present at microwave frequencies, while continuous-wave lasers require heterodyning modulation and detection which add complications to the system. There is very little frequency tuning available.

Most types of laser have been deployed in the tracking systems. Solid-state lasers such as ruby and Nd:YAG and the semi-conductor GaAs laser have all been used in Q-switched pulsed mode; while CO_2 He-Ne and Ar have been used in continuous working mode with external modulators.

The laser beam is usually expanded with a telescope in order to reduce the beam divergence and there are several ways of combining the laser with the telescope to direct the beam towards the target. An arrangement in which the beam is first expanded and then directed is called a coelostat and, if the beam is directed before expansion, the configuration is a Loudé telescope.

Some examples of laser tracking systems are outlined below.

A mobile van-mounted system has been developed by Sylvania and used for tracking co-operative aircraft. The system incorporates a Q-switched pulse Nd:YAG laser with output pulse of 50 mJ and width 15 ns, which is capable of operating at a maximum repetition frequency of 100 Hz. The optical arrangement is a coelostat with the final transmitting mirror being adjustable in azimuth and elevation to give continuous pointing coverage of the target. Acquisition is via a joystick-controlled vidicon television camera, with near-parallel bore sight and once the target is located in the television display the system goes into a fully automatic tracking mode. A retroreflecting array is attached to the aircraft in order to enhance the optical return signal which is passed back along the same boresight as the transmitter through the transmitting mirror and to a beam splitter, thence to a ranging receiver and a tracking receiver. The latter incorporates a silicon diode quadrant detector which produces electronic signals for servo-mechanisms to actuate the mirror for maintaining target station. The ranging receiver signal is used as a stop pulse in a range counter, measuring range in the same manner as described earlier for the rangefinder. The system is capable of tracking to an angular accuracy of 100μrad in azimuth and in elevation and can range to an accuracy between 0.2 and 1.5m, depending upon the strength of signal. Maximum range is about 30km and aircraft velocities up to 180 ms^{-1} and angular rates up to 2 rad s^{-1} are possible.

An example of a continuous-wave laser tracking system is to be found at White Sands Missile Range in New Mexico. This has been used for tracking missiles from launch with a range accuracy of about 0.1m and a tracking accuracy of 100μrad. The system uses an argon-ion laser of 5W output which is modulated and transmitted through a fully-adjustable mirror with a pointing accuracy of 50μrad. The beam is sufficiently narrow to ensure sufficient return signal without the aid of retroreflectors and this is applicable for engagement of hostile targets. The system is fully automatic and, unusually, acquisition is obtained by laser beam scattering over a field of view of ±1°. As the aim point is directed at the missile's nose, unwanted signal from the hot exhaust is much reduced.

Coherent Doppler trackers have also been developed offering superior signal-to-noise performance over direct detection methods of tracking.

The superior resolution of the laser tracker is offset by the narrow search cone, though this enables single targets to be selected. Scanning LADAR has been used for scene imaging by synchronising the laser beam with a scanning electro-optical receiver, but, because of the small instantaneous field of view of the laser beam, it takes much longer to plot an equivalent radar map. This might, however, be improved substantially by using high repetition frequency laser beams with higher power so that collimation may be relaxed and field of view increased.

A mixture of laser and radar trackers offers the best compromise and some systems employ microwave modulation of the laser beam for increased sensitivity. A high-power CO_2 Doppler system at MIT works in modulated continuous working mode with an associated radar and visual tracker for acquisition. The device is used for tracking co-operative targets to high accuracy.

The advent of directed-energy weapons will impose severe requirements for high accuracy aiming and tracking of fast moving and manoeuvring targets. A laser weapon, for example, is effective only if the beam can be aimed and maintained on a vulnerable point of the target until a kill has been achieved. For some tactical targets this may require tracking jitter being held to better than one micro-radian in order to achieve good overlapping of the laser damage spot during the period of engagement. If an active tracker, such as a subsidiary laser, were to be used, it would be important to choose one of the same wavelength as that of the weapon itself so that both experience as close as is possible the same atmospheric transmission effects, and each should use the same boresight. Alternatively, the high power laser weapon beam could be used for tracking as well as for inflicting damage by correlating the hot-spot which is produced with some reference point on the target using passive electro-optical techniques to record the images of these features (hot-spot tracking).

Examples of advanced laser weapon trackers are the US Navy and US Air Force Beam Directors, both developed, built and tested during the 1970s and the *Sealite* Beam Director which incorporates developments from these two systems.

Guidance Systems

Laser beams are being used to guide missiles on to their targets, greatly improving targeting accuracy and range of operation.

One method is known as semi-active laser (SAL) homing. The principle is to illuminate the target by a laser beam designator and a passive sensor on the missile tracks on to the target by homing on to the reflected laser energy. Two trackers are required in this mode of guidance if the designating station is separately based from the missile. Examples of systems working in this mode of operation are the GEC-Marconi LRMTS, the *Copperhead* laser-guided shell and the *PAVEWAY* laser-guided bomb.

Another method of guidance is by line of sight beam riding (LOSBR). The

LOSBR principle is to illuminate a receiver in the rear of the missile to maintain it on to the target co-ordinates by navigational means. GEC-Marconi have developed a continuous wave CO_2 laser system based upon this technique.

A third method of using a laser is by command to line of sight (CLOS) homing. This requires a target tracker and a missile tracker, the purpose being to maintain both tracking lines on to the same boresight. A beacon shining at the back of the missile is used for the missile-tracking source and the lateral acceleration of the missile required to bring it back on to the target line-of-sight is computed. Unlike LOSBR, a CLOS multi-missile system requires different commands for each missile launched at a single target. CLOS guidance is used by the *Rapier* low-level air defence system.

Inertial guidance systems can now make use of the ring laser gyroscope. In operation two laser beams of the same wavelength travel in opposite directions around a ring cavity. At one corner both beams are passed through a beam splitter and fed to photodiodes. The rate of rotation of the cavity is sensed by measuring the difference in frequencies between the two beams caused by one beam travelling further round the ring than the other, the difference being proportional to the rate of rotation. The difference is then fed to servos which direct the aim point. The advantages of laser gyroscopes over conventional mechanical types are that they are smaller, weigh less, are cheaper to produce, more stable, take less time to make a reading and are virtually maintenance-free. They have essentially no gravitational sensitivity, therefore can work in high-*g* environments and are much more highly linear, to parts per billion compared with parts per million, over a large dynamic range.

The future may reveal the laser in a major role as part of 'intelligent' weapon guidance systems in tactical scenarios, complementing advanced, passive, electro-optic sensors such as staring focal plane arrays. The latter systems are able to practice 'fire and forget' (F&F), provided that the target signature can be stored in the computer memory, but are said not to be effective against ATGM positions, for example. A laser does not suffer from this problem provided that it is manually operated and could be used to enhance the performance of the staring array.

Laser Warning Receivers

The increasing use of lasers on the battlefield calls for electro-optical countermeasures (EOCM) to augment radar warning receivers for ESM operations. Like its microwave counterpart, the laser warning receiver (LWR) serves to detect the radiation which is being beamed at the target so that countermeasures may be cued.

Ideally a LWR needs to identify the wavelength, energy, temporal and spatial profiles of the threat, its direction, bearing and range. It must have a low false-alarm rate, for instance, against reflections from other lasers on the battlefield and against EOCM. Detector systems need to have very high dynamic range and use logarithmic amplifiers for low noise and wide bandwidth.

LWR techniques are of three types, namely non-imaging, imaging and inter-ferometric. The non-imaging techniques have panoramic surveillance capability but only limited directional resolution, typically between 15 and 45°; a grating spectrometer may be incorporated to give wavelength discrimination. Imaging systems are based upon focal plane charge-coupled devices (CCD) and silicon position-sensitive detectors; the bearing of the threat is computed from the location of the focused spot on the range plane; this type is not capable of wavelength discrimination. Interferometric LWRs are able to test for coherence and provide both wavelength and bearing data; versions are based upon Michelson, Mach-Zender and Fabry-Perot interferometers.

No single type of LWR covers all requirements and those currently in operation give only limited threat data. They do not characterise the laser beam, give only rough azimuthal information and can be easily spoofed by a multi-laser threat. Future developments will concentrate on improving performance, particularly in areas of bearing, identification, state of polarisation and temporal profile of the laser threat. Testing of the spatial and temporal coherence of the incoming radiation is a clear interpretation that the threat arises from a laser and has the strong advantage over a measurement of intensity in being able to filter out incoherent noise signals from the background. Coherent optical detection is a part of the broader field of optical transform and range modulation processing techniques which are now being developed along the lines of the radar analogy.

Developments are to integrate LWRs with radar warning receivers and examples are to be found in Racal, Plessey, GEC-Marconi, MBB and Perkin-Elmer systems. The Racal system is called *Saviour* and is vehicle-mounted. The radar receiver operates in the frequency range 8.0 to 12.0 GHz and the laser receiver in the wavelength range 0.66 to 1.1μm. Displays in the vehicle indicate threat direction and whether it is radar or laser. GEC-Marconi Type 453 LWR covers 360° in azimuth and up to 180° in elevation, within a detector bandwidth from 0.3 to 1.5μm; the system has high spectral resolution to differentiate between different laser threats. MBB has a wide bandwidth into the far infra-red. Plessey's LWR employs a quadrant detector and distinguishes between rangefinders and designators. The Perkin-Elmer system is interferometric and uses a Fabry-Perot etalon to discriminate laser threats from the background.

Communications

Lasers offer great potential as a means of communication and are now being integrated into point-to-point and fibre-optic communication systems. The narrowness of the laser beam offers high directional aiming and good protection against interference. Lasers could be used for secure, short-range open communications. Like its microwave counterpart, the laser can be modulated to transmit either speech or pictures, by varying the amplitude of the beam with a shutter or by coding the pulses. The vast difference between them is the amount of information that can be carried by a laser beam. Even though the degree of modulation is lower with a laser beam, the higher frequency enables bandwidths of the order 100 MHz of voice channel or 100 kHz of TV channel, which are about one thousand times the microwave communication capacity. There are, of course, disadvantages, the main one being the atmosphere propagation loss.

Closed communication avoids the atmospheric transmission problem and is being examined by using fibre optics. Low-loss glass types have been developed and their potential for short-range communication tasks has been established. They have two major advantages over electrical systems. First, their weight reduction of about one order of magnitude over conventional systems makes them very attractive for lightweighting operations. Second, they are free from interference from neighbouring electrical systems and from electromagnetic pulse (EMP) from a nuclear explosion or from ESM. Gallium arsenide laser has attractive qualities for use in fibre-optic systems. Guided-wire systems are being replaced by fibre-optic equivalents.

Holography

Holograms work on the basis of coherent diffraction optics. The laser is used both to produce the hologram and to reconstruct the three-dimensional holographic image. Many holograms may be stored on a single plate and reconstructions achieved by illuminating the plate at an appropriate angle.

Holography is being used in aircraft head-up displays (HUDs) to provide the pilot with image symbology of flight co-ordinates which is superimposed at infinity on the pilot's view of the target scene.

Holograms offer better performance over HUDs that use conventional refractive optics, in particular, in increasing image brightness and field of view with the additional advantages of saving weight and space in the cockpit.

Direct Fire Simulation

Lasers are used as training aids for tank crews in precision gunnery against realistically moving targets, thus considerably easing the logistic problems, organisation, and ammunition costs associated with the conventional training exercises.

A typical laser-based simulator operates in the following way: when the engaging crew is satisfied that the weapon is laid on the target, the gunner presses the firing button. A flash generator fires and the laser mounted coaxially with the tank gun emits pulses for one or two seconds. These are picked up by detectors on the target which automatically transmits a 'hit' or 'miss' signal by radio, the result of which is indicated in the gunner's eyepiece. If a hit has been scored a smoke flare is ignited on the target, for instance, a tank, its radio deactivated and its own laser switched off. These may be reactivated by an umpire or after a pre-set delay.

A tank gun training simulator is called *Simfire*. It consists of a gallium arsenide laser emitting trains of pulses of 0.6 mJ and 100 ns width with repetition frequency ranging from 280 to 300 Hz. The system is operational from 400 to 2000m. The target detectors each cover 90° in azimuth and 35° in elevation; and four detectors are required to simulate a tank turret. The size of the target zone which will result in a 'kill' is 3m × 2m. The radio link is crystal controlled and operated at 79 MHz. The link is activated only when responding to laser pulses received by one of the detector units. It then responds, pulse for pulse, with 2μs pulses of approximately 20 W average power.

A similar system built by Saab-Scania and called the BT41 Tank Combat Simulator is in use with the Swedish Army. It features real-time simulation of the projectile flight, type of ammunition used and accurate simulation of target-vulnerability characteristics. The system also generates a realistic tracer simulation into the gunner's sight. The laser beam is coded by modulation and is used to convey information to the target of the relative position between laser beam and projectile position; thus the target obtains data on the type and co-ordinates of the passing projectile and the identity of the attacking unit. The target has 12 detectors with retroreflectors and thus two-way information processing is possible. The relevant kill-probability may be calculated from the co-ordinates of the projectile and the effect of the hit can be evaluated. The software enables varying conditional probabilities, such as chance of kill at second hit, to be evaluated. The BT41 can be used for training in direct fire gunnery for other targets, such as artillery and guided missiles, and target image simulators are built into the software.

A suite of direct fire weapon effect simulators are being deployed for training use with the British Army. These have been developed by Saab and cover a range of applications from rifle to tank-gun simulation.

Future Laser Radar Developments

Advances in laser radar techniques will depend upon technological developments such as more powerful and efficient lasers, higher pulse repetition rates, improved detection methods, electronics and computing facilities.

The emergence of the US Strategic Defense Initiative has given much momentum to the use of laser radar at high altitudes and in space where atmospheric attenuation is insignificant. An example is project DELTA 181, a space-based sensor package containing a pulsed LIDAR and a Doppler LADAR, which has recently been tested.

Examples of tactical systems under development are a Hughes and General Dynamics LADAR for a cruise missile guidance and stealth navigation system, a Vought system for attack aircraft, a Raytheon CO_2 system for anemometry and a Lincoln CO_2 LADAR. GEC-Marconi are currently developing the CLARA (Compact Laser Radar) demonstrator jointly with Dassault Electronique for both helicopter and fixed-wing aircraft.

Laser Safety

Hazard Effects

Lasers can cause damage to eyes and skin at the levels of intensity used in operational training. This arises through absorption of laser energy in biological tissues, causing local heating and chemical, thermal or thermomechanical effects. The effect of the damage is related to the wavelength and temporal profile of the beam, the size of the laser source and time over which the tissue is exposed.

Two important wavelength regions may be identified in so far as damage to the eye is concerned. The first of these is between 0.4μm and 1.4μm and poses the greatest hazard. Radiation within this bandwidth passes through the front ocular structure of the eye (the cornea, the lens and the humours) with little absorption and is then focused to a very small spot (~10μm) on the retina, resulting in possible permanent damage to this sensitive organ. The intensity of the radiation on the retina could be up to half a million times greater than that which is normally incident upon it and the effect is particularly severe if the eye is relaxed and looking direct into the laser beam. In such a situation the whole of the radiation falls on the fovea, that part of the retina of about 1.5mm diameter on which the ability for chromatic viewing and detailed vision is dependent. Glancing laser radiation focuses on to less vital parts of the retina but nevertheless impairs efficiency.

The second region of wavelength is really two regions, namely wavelengths less than 0.3μm and greater than 1.4μm. In these virtually no laser radiation penetrates to the retina but is mainly absorbed in the cornea, the eye lens and the humours. Because there is no focusing effect for corneal irradiation, the laser intensity to cause damage is much greater and the hazard is much reduced.

The conclusion is that lasers in the visible and, to a lesser extent, near infra-red region, e.g, ruby, argon, neodymium (1.06μm and 0.53μm) are much more hazardous than the far infra-red (carbon dioxide) and ultraviolet (excimer) lasers.

The time of exposure is important because of the limitations of conducting the heat away from the exposed organ to reduce temperature and damage. Thus for a given source power or energy pulsed lasers are more injurious than CW lasers of the same wavelength. Visible lasers, which may be considered as point sources, are more hazardous than extended sources, such as laser diode arrays, because they produce a higher degree of convergence on the retina.

Laser Standards

The current international laser safety standard IEC 825–1 and the derived British Standard EN60825 give a system of laser classification depending upon the degree of hazard. These are grouped into five classes. Class I lasers are unequivocally eye-safe and have no restrictions; Class II are low-power visible lasers where protection is effected by blink reflex; Class IIIA lasers require protection if binoculars are used; Class IIIB lasers are visible or invisible and may cause injury to the unprotected eye but are safe when viewing diffuse reflections; and Class IV lasers may inflict injury to eyes and skin and cause other hazards such as ignition of materials; they are dangerous even when viewing a diffuse surface and must be totally contained.

Hazard evaluation is a complex process and beyond the scope of this chapter. It is fully described in JSP 390, *Military Laser Safety 1996*, which is the official guide for the UK Armed Services and Ministry of Defence organisations and is compatible with the NATO Standard STANAG 3606.

Hazard Evaluation

JSP 390 adopts two approaches to hazard evaluation these being: *deterministic modelling* which is used for scenarios involving static ground laser firing at fixed ground targets on controlled outdoor ranges, and *probabilistic modelling* for highly mobile laser air platforms in air-to-ground engagements over UK ranges.

The general features of these modelling approaches are summarised below, for illustrative purposes, *but expert advice must always be obtained before undertaking hazard calculations on specific systems*.

Deterministic modelling is based upon the parameters maximum permissible exposure (MPE) and nominal ocular hazard distance (NOHD), which are defined below.

The *maximum permissible exposure* (MPE) is defined as that intensity of laser radiation incident at the cornea below which exposed persons will not suffer adverse visible effects. It is analogous and equivalent to the Protection Standard (PS) which is used in STANAG 3606. MPE/PS for some specific cases are shown in Table 6.5.

It may be seen from this table that ruby has the lowest MPE and is the most hazardous. By contrast, CO_2 has the highest MPE which for CW operation is only a factor of two higher than ambient black-body conditions. The reader is referred to the full tabular data, which are complex, for general cases.

Table 6.5 Maximum Permissible Exposure (Protection Standard)

Type of Laser	Output	Wavelength μm		MPE/PS at the Cornea
ruby	single pulse	0.694	1 ns–18μs	$5 \times 10\text{-}3$ Jm^{-2}
neodymium	single pulse	1.06	1 ns–50μs	$5 \times 10\text{-}3$ Jm^{-2}
carbon dioxide	single pulse	10.6	1 ns–11 ns	100 Jm^{-2}
carbon dioxide	CW	10.6	> 10 s	1000 Wm^{-2}

Source: extracted from IEC 825–1/JSP 390/STANAG (for illustration purposes only)

The nominal ocular hazard distance (NOHD) is defined as the distance along the axis of the beam from the laser beyond which the laser intensity has fallen below the level of the MPE for the unaided eye. It assumes the laser beam emerges from the exit aperture in the far-field, a gaussian beam profile and no account is taken of atmospheric or other effects. It is given by the following expression:

$$\text{NOHD} = \frac{1}{\phi} \left[\left(\frac{1.27\, Q}{\text{MPE}} \right)^{1/2} - a \right] \qquad (11)$$

where
Q = laser pulse energy (J) or power (W),
MPE = MPE or Protection Standard (normally J m^{-2} or Wm^{-2}),
ϕ = beam divergence (radians),
a = emergent beam diameter at 1/e of the peak intensity.

Approximate values of NOHDs for some of the laser equipments of interest are given in Table 6.6.

Table 6.6 Approximate Nominal Ocular Hazard Distances

Laser	NOHD
Chieftain ruby LF2	10km
SIMRAD LP7	3km
LRMTS	20km
CO2 laser (2W)	0km

Magnifying optics increase the collecting power, typically by $K = \tau M^2$ where τ is the transmittance of the optics and M is the magnification. The effect is to increase the NOHD by a factor $\sqrt{K}$ to an Extended NOHD (ENOHD).

Further corrections need to be applied for repetitively pulsed lasers, for the use of attenuating filters and safety goggles and for conditions where the beam is not gaussian in profile. Proprietary goggles are available which are marked with the attenuation they provide against the laser radiation wavelength from which they are designed to protect.

Atmospheric factors are dealt with in JSP 390. The effects of atmospheric attenuation (reducing hazard) and of turbulence-produced scintillation (increasing hazard) are evaluated in this Standard.

MPE/PS levels are set well above observable injury criteria and as such are regarded as highly pessimistic, as is the NOHD which is calculated from them. These deterministic criteria are less suitable for highly-mobile, laser air platforms, particularly in air-to-ground engagements. In these scenarios, the use of MPE criteria may lead to unrealistically large ground laser-hazard footprints which may even extend outside the range boundary. This is of particular importance with respect to geographically-limited UK ranges and the consequent problems in meeting military training requirements for the use of laser devices.

In such cases an alternative probabilistic modelling method based upon risk assessment of hazard is adopted which does not compromise laser safety. This approach is based upon the concept that a casual observer beyond the range boundary may be irradiated with an acceptably low probability, resulting in a minimal level of eye damage which can be measured by an ophthalmoscope. This level of ocular damage is called the minimum ophthalmoscopically visible lesion (MOVL), which would incur an insignificant level of visual impairment in creating a retinal lesion of 30μm. MOVL replaces MPE in probabilistic hazard assessment.

There is no equivalent to the NOHD in the probabilistic model, but it is replaced by a *laser hazard area trace* (LHAT), inside which the risk of ocular damage is deemed to be unacceptable. Typically, this level is chosen to be 10^{-8} per engagement on the boundary to give realistic pessimism without inflicting a higher level of ocular damage and compares favourably with other military weapon risk criteria. It should be stressed that the choice of these parameters, within a probabilistic approach, does not invoke higher levels of risk of receiving ocular impairment than those which are implied by irradiation at the level of MPE.

Laser Eye Protection

Most current laser rangefinders and designators have sufficient power to cause damage to eyes and to sensors. The protection of eyes, in particular, is an essential requirement and is addressed here.

There are two basic technologies that have been used to manufacture laser goggles, based upon absorption and reflection.

Absorbing glasses are abundant and attenuate over a wide range of wavelengths. They operate over broad bands and thus may impair visibility; they also are inclined to be heavy and have limited impact resistance. They are made from injection-moulded plastics containing dyes which can have spectral properties ranging from narrow to broad band. There is abundant choice in the visible and the ultraviolet but less in the near infra-red. Polycarbonate as host material is commonly used, making for cheapness and higher impact strength over glasses but lower transmittance. Such dyes are favoured for pilot eye protection because they offer wider angular protection when compared to the reflection techniques.

Reflection technologies enable specific wavelength or very narrow wavelength bands to be selectively reflected by optical interference. These take the form of multi-layer interference films which are laid down on an optical substrate by vacuum coating or in the form of a hologram. Such techniques reduce the unwanted transmission radiation level down to 0.01 per cent without impairing wanted visibility, but are limited in angular protection to about ±40°.

Vacuum-coated goggles are limited to a maximum number of three wavelengths that can be rejected by a single goggle because each wavelength requires its own set of multilayer interference films and thus weight may become a difficulty. Though glass has commonly been used for the optical substrate it has low impact strength making it unsuitable for eye protection and other materials are now being researched. The problems of vacuum coating on curved surfaces is being overcome.

Holography is a relatively new technique and the search for stable holographic materials which can be applied to large polycarbonate substrates is an important objective. The most well-established holographic material, dichromated gelatin, is degraded by water vapour and has to be protected by lamination between glass.

Forward objectives are to achieve wide angular coverage and good wavelength rejection without impairing overall visibility. The solution may ultimately be achieved by developments in holography.

The protection techniques which have been described are passive, that is they have a fixed spectral performance. They would be ineffective in protection against a wavelength-tunable laser and for these situations recourse has to be found in the use of active technologies, in other words, the spectral performance is modified by the incident laser radiation. Such technologies come within the scope of non-linear optics.

As it appears unlikely that wavelength-agile lasers will be dedicated to rangefinding and designating, any further discussion of their techniques is beyond the scope of this chapter.

7

•••••••••

Radar Systems

INTRODUCTION

Radar is an electronic system for the detection and location of objects and their movement. It does this by beaming electromagnetic waves at them and analysing the echoes. The basic principle is illustrated in Figure 7.1.

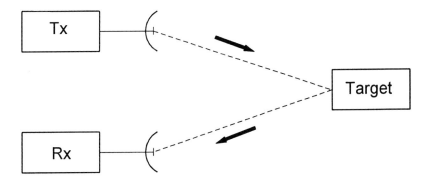

Figure 7.1 Basic Radar Principle

Radio frequency power is produced by the transmitter (usually high power) and fed to the transmitting antenna. The antenna then radiates this power in the form of a narrow 'searchlight' beam of electromagnetic (EM) radiation. This travels outwards from the antenna, striking any object that is within the beam. Reflections from any such object (a target) are received by the receiving aerial, and fed into the receiver for analysis. From this analysis it is possible to obtain the following information about the target:

• *Range*. Range may be obtained by measurement of the transit time of the signal from transmitter to receiver via the target (echo time). Knowing the velocity of the EM radiation, the total round trip distance may be found, and hence the target range;

- *Range rate.* Any target motion towards or away from the radar (radial velocity) causes the radar's transmission frequency to be altered on reflection. This effect is known as the Doppler shift. Measurement of the Doppler shift in the received echo therefore allows the radial velocity (range rate) of the target to be found;
- *Direction.* The direction in which the receiving aerial is pointing when the echo is received gives information on target direction. A narrow horizontal beamwidth allows the determination of azimuth, while a narrow vertical beamwidth allows the determination of elevation;
- *Shape and size.* Limited indication of the size and shape of the target may be obtained from the amplitude of the echo signal and from the way that this amplitude varies as the target changes aspect relative to the receiving aerial;
- *Identification.* Signal processing techniques are getting rapid enough to allow target classification and identification to be carried out by a very detailed analysis of the target echo. This process, known as non-co-operative target recognition, or NCTR, is still a somewhat immature technique but shows great promise for the future.

Having obtained this information, which can be continually updated, it is possible to track, and if necessary intercept, the target.

Quality of Radar Performance

The primary function of a radar is to detect the presence of a target and measure its parameters. The degree to which a radar is able to carry out this function determines the quality of the radar. The primary considerations when assessing radar performance are:

- *Reliability of detection.* When power is transmitted, the signal travels away from the radar, striking anything in its path, and returning as echoes. These echoes will arrive as a sequence, with those from nearby targets arriving first, followed by those from more distant targets. The radar receiver is required to detect each echo (i.e., decide that a target is present) in the presence of electrical noise, which exists in all electrical systems. It does this by setting a threshold level and deciding that a target is present whenever the threshold is exceeded. The trick is to set the threshold low enough that it detects the targets, but high enough to prevent noise spikes from crossing it and being flagged up as targets. In practice, this can fail in two ways:

1. The signal can remain undetected (missed target). This can happen whenever the received signal is partially cancelled by the noise signal, dragging it below the threshold. Thus any given target will not be detected with 100

per cent probability, giving a *probability of detection* (P_d) of less than 100 per cent.

2. A noise spike can occasionally cross the threshold and be wrongly interpreted by the receiver as a target return (false alarm). Thus a radar produces a random succession of false alarms. The average rate at which it does this is known as its *false alarm rate* (FAR).

These two situations are shown in Figure 7.2.

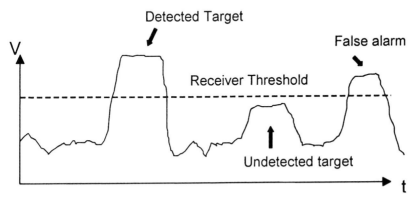

Figure 7.2 Radar Detection

Clearly it is desirable to produce a radar that detects targets 100 per cent of the time and produces no false alarms, and the extent to which it succeeds in this determines its reliability of detection. Users of radar systems define what is an acceptable probability of detection and an acceptable false alarm rate. However, it is clear from Figure 7.2 that the echo can be too weak to set a threshold which meets these requirements. This leads to the concept of a minimum echo strength for satisfactory detection (*minimum detectable signal*). In practice this is typically around 10^{-13} to 10^{-14} watts.

- *Accuracy.* This is a measure of the expected error in the measurement of the range, velocity, or angular position of the target.
- *Discrimination.* A radar's ability to detect or track a target in the presence of environmental echoes (clutter), or in the presence of other unwanted signals, is the discrimination of the radar. Perhaps it should be emphasised that this property applies to detection against a background of other real echoes, and not to the detection of targets in noise, or in enemy noise jamming.
- *Ambiguity.* It is possible under certain conditions for a radar to give false or ambiguous indications of range, range rate or direction. Its immunity from ambiguous interpretation is an important factor when assessing radar performance.

- *Resolution.* The resolution of a radar is a measure of the minimum separation in range, range rate or direction required between two targets in order for the system to detect them as two individual targets, rather than as a single one.
- *Countermeasure immunity.* This parameter is a measure of the radar's ability to continue to give useful and reliable information in the presence of enemy radiation designed to degrade the radar performance.

Radar Types and Radar Tasks

Radars may be divided into various categories depending upon the principle of operation and the location of the transmitter and receiver.

- *Primary radar.* A primary radar is a system which relies upon the reflection of energy from the intended target. The target is passive and the amount of energy reflected is dependent upon the radar cross section of the target and the incident energy. The majority of radars in use today fall into this category.
- *Secondary radar.* This type of radar relies upon active co-operation from the target. The target normally has a transmitter and receiver on board (known as a transponder). The transponder detects the pulse from the radar and replies with a coded transmission. Normally the transmitted pulse from the transponder is on a different frequency to the radar. This technique is used to keep track of aircraft. The coded reply from the aircraft gives details of the target's identity, height, speed, etc.
- *Monostatic.* For this type of radar the transmitter and receiver are co-located and often use the same antenna. Hence a target, by being aware of the direction from which the transmitted energy came, will also know the direction of the receiver. This is important in military applications when one may wish to send false information back to the receiver or present a low radar cross section.
- *Bistatic and multistatic.* In a bistatic radar system the transmitter and receiver are positioned in different locations. The separation can vary from a few hundred metres to a hundred kilometres or so. The system is not confined to one receiver. Several receiver systems may be operated with one common transmitter.

The use of radar has increased very greatly over the past 40 years, as has its variety. Radar systems in current use now range from simple systems designed to detect and locate targets (simple pulse) or measure their range rate (continuous wave), to systems designed to do these things in the presence of high levels of clutter (pulse Doppler, MTI). Radar equipments that reliably locate and track single or multiple targets (monopulse, track-while-scan), control weapon release (fire control), guide a weapon on to the target (guidance) and control the detonation of the warhead (fusing), are in common use. Modern radars can use sophisticated techniques to give high resolution in range and angle (pulse compression and synthetic aperture), giving the capability to produce high resolution ground maps.

Radar Transmission Frequencies

Radar has traditionally used radio frequencies in the microwave region. This consists of frequencies from about 1 Gigahertz (1000 Megahertz) up to 30 GHz. This corresponds to wavelengths running from 30cm down to 1cm. Above 30 GHz lies the millimetric band, where wavelengths fall to less than 1cm, and currently radars are beginning to exploit this band also. Some radar equipments, particularly non-western, can also be found in the region below 1 GHz. Figure 7.3 illustrates the whole range, giving the NATO and civilian nomenclature for the various specific transmission bands.

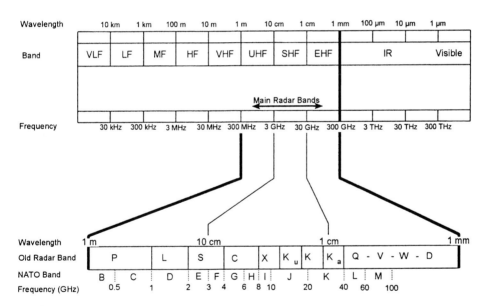

Figure 7.3 Radar Frequencies

The frequency of transmission has a significant bearing on the radar's capabilities, and hence on its uses. The main considerations are given below:

- *Size.* Radar equipments tend to be scaled with wavelength. Thus radars operating at 1 GHz (30cm) tend to be large and immobile. On the other hand, 10 GHz produces equipment sizes that are ideal for inclusion in aircraft, and 15 GHz produces systems that can be carried fairly easily;

161

- *Power and range.* Large equipments tend to high-power equipments, and hence are able to get echoes back from considerable range, that are still strong enough for detection. Small equipments have much lower power capability, and hence cannot 'see' targets so far away;
- *Resolution.* The ability to separate closely-spaced targets improves with increasing frequency. (This aspect is discussed later.)

The result of these points is that long-range (100s of km) radars are low frequency (1–3 GHz), large (10s to 100s of tons) systems, which are not easy to move, if, indeed, they can be moved at all. Mobile and man-portable systems, on the other hand, have to be small and light, and consequently tend to be low-power, high-frequency (10–20 GHz), and short range (10s of km at most). Table 7.1 below gives some indication of these trends. (Note that these figures *are* designed to show trends. They are therefore generic only.)

Table 7.1

Role	Range (km)	Frequency	Peak Tx Power	Size
ICBM detection	2000–3000	400–500 MHz	5–10 MW	Building 30 metres high
Long range AD	400–700	1–3 GHz	1–2 MW	Transportable on a number of trailers; antenna 6 × 4 metres; large cabin for operators
Med range AD	50–200	5–6 GHz	10–20 kW	Mobile on tracked or wheeled vehicle
Battlefield surv	5–20	10–20 GHz	1–1000 W	Two-man portable
Mortar homing	0.5–1.5	94 GHz	10–20 W	Fits inside 90mm mortar round

Pros and Cons of Radar as Compared with Other Sensors

Radar has a number of characteristics that make it different from other sensors. These are:

- Its active nature, which allows it to measure range and velocity;

- The choice of wavelength, which allows good penetration of the atmosphere and the weather; and
- Its relatively poor resolution.

These characteristics allow it to be:

- All-weather, day/night;
- Long-range;
- Capable of detecting small moving targets; and
- Ideal for autoalarm systems.

However, it suffers from:

- Being active; and
- Being unsuitable for imaging purposes.

Notwithstanding these last two, radar is unrivalled in long- to medium-range detection, and is frequently used in this capacity.

PULSE RADAR

In order to measure the transit time of the transmitted signal, and hence the target range, it is necessary to modulate the transmitter output in some way. One obvious way of doing this is by amplitude modulating the sinusoidal radio frequency output with a pulse train. The radar is then called a *pulse radar*. A block diagram of a typical simple pulse radar is shown in Figure 7.4.

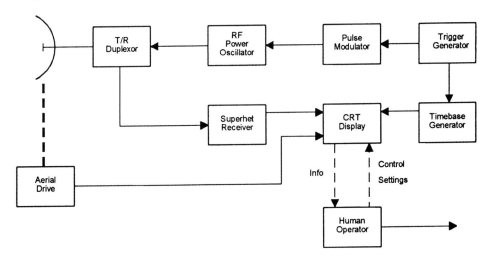

Figure 7.4 Block Diagram of a Pulse Radar

The trigger generator determines the pulse repetition frequency (f_r). It is used to trigger the transmitter and at the same time start the timebase for the range measurement. The pulse modulator is a high-power monostable multivibrator circuit which determines the pulse width (τ). Its output consists of a string of narrow pulses of frequency f_r which are used to modulate the output of a high-power r.f. valve. In older radars, this valve was usually a high-power r.f. oscillator (normally a multi-cavity magnetron) which was switched on and off by the modulator. In more recent times, however, the tendency has been to have a low-power oscillator running continuously, with the modulator controlling a high-power r.f. amplifier (a multi-cavity klystron, or, most recently, a travelling-wave tube (TWT)). The relevant waveforms for both cases are shown in Figure 7.5.

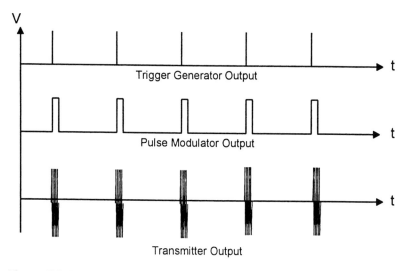

Figure 7.5 Transmitter Waveforms

Returning echoes are fed via a common aerial and a duplexer to the receiver, where they are amplified, detected, and fed to the CRT display. Here they are combined with directional information from the aerial drive. Traditionally, the decision regarding the presence or absence of a target was made by the human operator looking at the CRT; nowadays, however, there is an increasing trend towards automatic target detection. In this case the receiver output is not fed directly to a CRT, but to suitable decision circuitry instead. The circuitry then displays to the human operator only those targets that it has decided are present. (This technique is known as *automatic plot extraction.*) The advent of plot extraction has also allowed a move away from the conventional type of plan position indicator (PPI) towards the synthetic raster display.

Transmitted Waveform, Power and Duty Cycle

Figure 7.6 shows the modulating pulse train which controls the transmitter output:

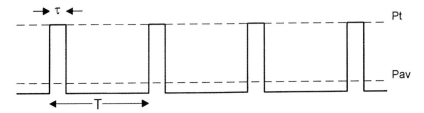

Figure 7.6 Transmitter Waveform – Definitions

The pulse width is τ, and the pulse repetition period is T. The modulating frequency (pulse repetition frequency, f_r) is given by:

$$f_r = 1/T$$

and is usually of the order of 1,000 pps. This frequency should be carefully distinguished from the transmitting frequency of the radar, which is usually in the gigahertz range (although recently some radars operating at much lower frequencies have started to come into use).

A glance at Figure 7.6 shows that the transmitter delivers power only for a fraction of the time. This fraction is known as the *Duty Cycle*, and is given by the expression:

$$\text{Duty Cycle} = \tau/T$$

Since $f_r = 1/T$, the duty cycle may also be written as

$$\text{Duty Cycle} = \tau f_r$$

The power being delivered by the transmitter during a pulse is known as the peak power (P_t). As the radar is not delivering this power all the time, the average power (P_{av}) is very much less than this. The relationship may be found by considering the energy contained in one pulse. This may be expressed as

$$E = \tau P_t$$

or as:

$$E = T P_{av}$$

165

Equating gives:

$$P_{av} = P_t \tau / T$$

Typically, pulse widths are of the order of 1μs, and Duty Cycles 1:1000. Peak powers may be megawatts and average powers, therefore, kilowatts.

Range Measurement

Target range (R) is found by measuring the time (t) taken for a pulse to travel to the target and back to the receiver. Knowing the velocity of EM radiation, and halving the round trip distance to get the one-way range, we have:

$$R = ct/2, \text{ where } c \text{ is the velocity of EM radiation}$$

Use of the above shows that an echo time of 1μs corresponds to a range of 150m (164 yards or 0.081 nautical miles). The nautical mile is the accepted unit of distance, but in some instances, where accuracy is secondary to convenience, the radar mile is used. This is 2,000 yards and differs from the nautical mile by about one per cent. Approximate echo times per unit distance are 10μs per mile, 12μs per nautical mile, and 6⅔μs per kilometre.

Maximum Unambiguous Range

Once the transmitted pulse is emitted, sufficient time must elapse to allow all echoes to return before the next pulse is transmitted. Therefore the pulse repetition frequency is determined by the largest range at which targets are expected. If f_r is too high, then echoes may return after the next transmitted pulse, and range ambiguity will result. This situation is illustrated in Figure 7.7.

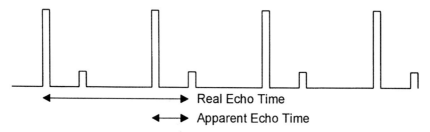

Figure 7.7 Maximum Unambiguous Range

Such echoes are termed *second time around echoes*, and should be avoided. The range beyond which target echoes appear as second time around echoes is termed the *maximum unambiguous range*, and is given by

$$R_{mu} = c/2f_r$$

Range Resolution

A simple pulse radar cannot separate two returning echoes if they overlap in time. This will occur if the two echo times differ by less than the pulse width, as shown in Figure 7.8.

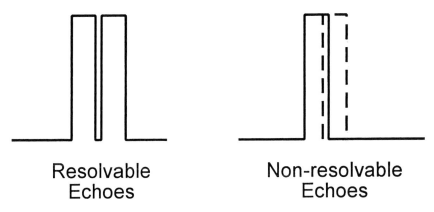

Resolvable
Echoes

Non-resolvable
Echoes

Figure 7.8 Range Resolution

Thus, to be resolved, the two targets must differ in range by at least $c\tau/2$, and hence the range resolution is given by

$$\Delta R = c\tau/2$$

Minimum Range

In order to protect the receiver from damage, it is necessary to disconnect it during the transmitter pulse. Thus the receiver cannot receive any echo which returns during this time. Further, the T/R cell which is used to isolate the receiver takes a short time to recover after the transmitted pulse has left the radar, and the receiver will fail to receive any echo which returns during this period also. Thus the echo time of any target must be at least the pulse width plus T/R cell recovery time (t_{TR}) if it is to be detected. Thus the radar has a minimum detection range which is given by:

$$R_{min} = c(\tau + t_{TR})/2$$

Receiver Bandwidth

The superheterodyne receiver of a typical pulse radar consists of a crystal mixer followed by an IF amplifier, followed by a detector and video stages. This is illustrated in Figure 7.9:

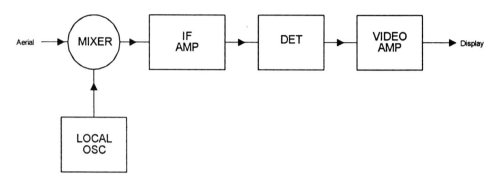

Figure 7.9 Superheterodyne Receiver

The bandwidth required by the IF stage is dictated by the frequency spectrum of the received signal. This naturally depends on the frequency spectrum of the transmitted signal. Figure 7.10 shows the frequency spectrum of pulse modulated r.f., with a pulse repetition frequency of f_r and a pulse width of τ.

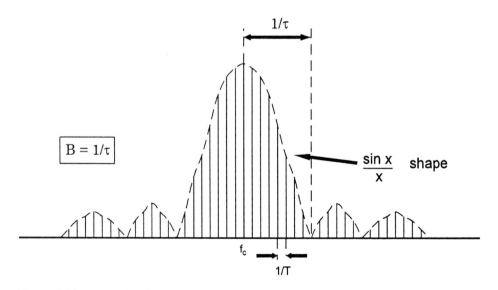

Figure 7.10 Transmitted Spectrum

It is a $\sin x/x$ envelope containing a line spectrum centred on the r.f. carrier frequency, and with line spacing of f_r. It has an infinite bandwidth. In practice,

168

however, the bandwidth will be limited by the frequency constraints of the transmitter circuitry. This causes the leading and trailing edges of the pulse to slope somewhat, and the transmitted signal will be of finite, but large, bandwidth.

If the receiver is to cope accurately with the signal, therefore, it must have the same very wide bandwidth. Now, since thermal noise in a receiver is proportional to bandwidth, this large bandwidth will allow a large quantity of noise into the receiver. This makes the receiver insensitive to the signals that we want to detect. Reduction in the bandwidth will improve this situation, but at the expense of pulse shape. Actually, the pulse shape is not a particularly vital parameter in a radar system. After all, the important thing is detection. Therefore the tendency has been to optimise the receiver to give the best detection capability and to allow pulse shape to suffer. A receiver which optimises in this way is normally known as a *matched receiver* (or matched filter). In practice such a receiver has a bandwidth of $1/\tau$. Figure 7.11 illustrates this loss of pulse shape. Here the detected signal has a completely different shape to the transmitted pulse. However, the amplitude is higher in the detected signal and hence easier to detect.

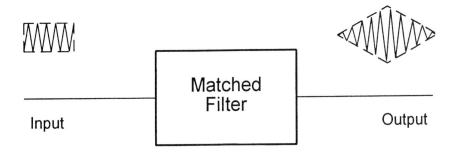

Figure 7.11 Matched Filter

If preserving the pulse shape is important, other receiver techniques must be employed. This invariably involves using large bandwidths (up to $5/\tau$ in older radars). This allows timing to be done on the leading edge of the echo, but degrades the radar's detection performance because the receiver is not matched. Leading-edge detection (common in the past) is not the preferred approach nowadays. However, certain radar equipments which use this method are still in service.

Radar Range Equation for Pulsed Radars

So far we have looked at parameters such as PRF, pulse width etc. which will determine some of the basic performance characteristics of the radar. However, before any target can be detected the power arriving back at the receiver must be sufficient for the target to be detected in the presence of noise or other interference. Consider free space conditions with the peak power radiated from the transmitter as P, the target at a range R and an antenna gain G, then the power density at the target will be:

$$\frac{PG}{4\pi R^2} \text{ watts/m}^2$$

If the effective reflecting area of the target is σ m^2 (typical values are tank: 5m^2; man: 1m^2; fighter aircraft: 10m^2; artillery shell: 0.001m^2; RPV: 0.1m^2) the power reradiated is:

$$\frac{PG\sigma}{4\pi R^2} \text{ watts}$$

and the power density at the receiving aerial, assuming isotropic radiation from the target, is:

$$\frac{PG\sigma}{(4\pi)^2 R^4} \text{ watts/m}^2$$

The available signal power to the receiver from the aerial, assuming an aerial aperture A_e, is:

$$S = \frac{PGA_e\sigma}{(4\pi)^2 R^4} \text{ watts}$$

If the minimum detectable signal power is defined as S_{min}, then the maximum detection range will be given by:

$$R^4_{max} = \frac{PGA_e\sigma}{(4\pi)^2 S_{min}}$$

(If we are using the same aerial for reception and transmission, antenna gain and aperture are related by:

$$A_e = \frac{G\lambda^2}{4\pi}$$

and we need only know G or A_e, rather than both, to use the equation.)

The things to note from the range equation are:

- the detection range of the radar depends on the fourth root of the transmitted power;
- the detection range depends on the fourth root of S_{min}; this in turn depends on the receiver sensitivity; and
- the detection range is proportional to antenna size.

Minimum Detectable Signal

The above equation could now be used to calculate the detection range of a radar. However, first it is necessary to put a value to S_{min}. This is driven by the need to detect the target with the required certainty in the presence of receiver noise. This reliability is normally stated as a design requirement in terms of a minimum probability of detection and a maximum false-alarm rate. For most radars, this is achieved if the S/N ratio is in the region of 14–16 dB. Since modern radars generate around 10^{-15} watts of receiver noise, it follows that S_{min} is typically in the region of 10^{-13}–10^{-14} watts.

Losses

This discussion has ignored the possibility that power is lost on the journey from transmitter via target to receiver. In practice, losses do take place, and they are significant.

- *System losses*. Losses caused by leakage, heating, and inefficiency exist within the radar itself (system losses). These reduce the detection range of the radar, modifying the range equation as shown below:

$$R^4_{max} = \frac{PGA_e\sigma}{(4\pi)^2 S_{min}L_{sys}}$$

These losses are frequency dependent (tending to rise with frequency), but a good rule of thumb figure to use is 10 dB. Thus radars require typically ten times more transmitter power than might have been thought. If transmitter power is not raised to compensate, this factor shortens detection ranges by a factor of 1.78.

● *Amospheric losses.* Two different losses take place in the atmosphere as the radar energy travels through it. There is attenuation caused by the air itself, normally known as clear air attenuation; this is present in all conditions. Attenuation is also caused by bad weather. In this case, raindrops, hailstones, etc., cause scattering and attenuation as they fall through the air. Both forms of attenuation rise with transmitter frequency. Once again the range equation needs to be modified, this time to give:

$$R^4_{max} = \frac{PGA_e\sigma}{(4\pi)^2 S_{min}L_{sys}L_{atmos}}$$

Atmospheric losses are exponential in nature, and hence this loss (one-way) is of the form $10^{\alpha R}$ where α is measured in Bels per kilometre. (A Bel is a logarithmic unit equal to 10 of the more familiar dB.) Converting this to an expression using dBs rather than Bels, and allowing for the two-way path gives $10^{0.2\alpha R}$ where α is now in dBs per kilometre. Thus we have the loss in the form:

$$L_{atmos} = 10^{(0.2\,\alpha R)}$$

This can be evaluated and used in the range equation, provided we know α. This can be looked up on a suitable graph. Figure 7.12 shows attenuation for clear air and for bad weather, in dBs per km (one-way).

Pulse Integration

The equation derived above is for a single echo. By integrating a number of echoes it is possible to improve the detection capabilities of the radar, and hence to reduce the required minimum detectable signal output from the receiver.

As the target is scanned by the radar beam, it is struck by a number of pulses, and hence returns a number of echoes. This number, n, is given by:

$$n = \frac{\theta_B f_r}{\omega_s}$$

where ω_s is the antenna scan rate in degrees/second. If ω_s is given in r.p.m., this becomes

$$n = \frac{\theta_B f_r}{6\omega_s}$$

If n pulses are added together, they can be made to form a single, integrated echo n times as large. The noise is also integrated, but because it is different from moment to moment, there is partial cancellation. This means that the echo grows in strength faster than the noise and becomes easier to detect. Therefore adding pulses together after they leave the receiver but before the display, improves detection, ideally by a factor of n. In practice the process of integration is not entirely efficient, and therefore the improvement is not the full n, but only a fraction of it. This fraction, $E_i(n)$, is known as the integration efficiency, and the total improvement is $nE_i(n)$. The value of $E_i(n)$ depends on probabilities of detection and false alarm, and on n itself. However, in most situations a figure of 0.7 is considered to be accurate enough. Thus one should place the factor of $nE_i(n)$ (typically $n \times 0.7$) on the top line of the equation and now the range can be found from:

$$R^4_{max} = \frac{PGA_e \sigma n E_i(n)}{(4\pi)^2 \, S_{min} L_{sys} L_{atmos}}$$

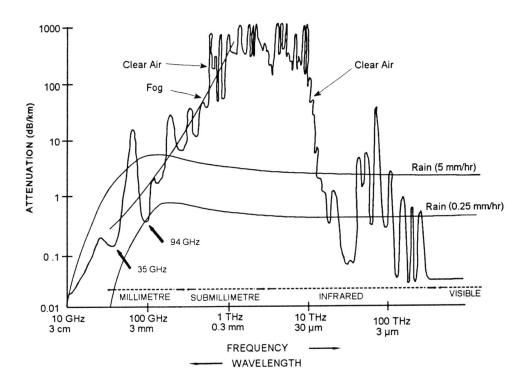

Figure 7.12 Atmospheric Attenuation

Pulse Compression

It has been stated already that the signal must compete with receiver noise. In practice, receiver noise is white noise and is evenly distributed across the frequency spectrum. Thus the amount of receiver noise that competes with the signal will depend on the bandwidth of the receiver. This bandwidth can be narrowed in design by the use of long transmitter pulses. This degrades the range resolution of the radar. To recover it, pulse compression may be used. This involves the transmission of a long pulse which is frequency-swept during the pulse. On reception, the pulse can be compressed by slowing the frequencies at the front of the echo, thus allowing the back of the echo to catch up. The pulse thus shortens in the receiver, restoring the range resolution.

Design Considerations for Pulse Radar Types

It is instructive at this point to consider the practical considerations which go into the design of different types of pulse radar.

Long-Range Search Radar

When designing a search radar the most important criterion is detection at the greatest range possible. Therefore high average transmitter power and low atmospheric losses are required. Both these considerations dictate a low frequency. It is also desirable to have a large aerial. This gives better detection in its own right, but is also required to give good angle resolution at low frequency. The long detection range dictates a large maximum unambiguous range, which means a low pulse repetition frequency (PRF). The low PRF dictates a slow scan rate, in order to give a reasonable number of hits per scan. The receiver sensitivity is ideally high, which implies low receiver noise. This requires a narrow bandwidth, which in turn dictates a large pulse width. This reduces the range resolution, but this is not an important factor at long ranges.

The parameters of a typical search radar are set out below:

frequency	3 GHz
peak power	2.25 MW
pulse width	5μS
PRF	300 pps
aerial size	15m × 5m
aerial beamwidths	0.5° × 1.5°
aerial gain	45 dB

scan rate	4 rpm
range	up to 250 nmi

Surface Surveillance Radar

At the other end of the scale, this radar is short range but requires extremely high resolution and frequent updates on data. These requirements imply a very narrow pulse width, and a high scan rate. Good azimuth resolution requires a narrow azimuth beamwidth. This implies an aerial structure many wavelengths in size, and hence a high frequency will be employed. The high scan rate dictates a high PRF to give a reasonable number of hits per scan. A small minimum range is desirable, which, in addition to the narrow pulse width, makes a very rapid recovery of the TR cell necessary. The short pulse implies a large receiver bandwidth. Typical parameters are:

frequency	24 GHz
peak power	50 kW
pulse width	0.02µs
PRF	14,000 pps
aerial size	3m × 1m
scan rate	60 rpm
t_{TR}	0.05µs

Secondary Radar

So far we have dealt only with systems that receive their own transmitted power reflected from a target. Here we deal with systems where the target responds to the transmitted pulse by sending an answer of its own. This answer contains information which is useful to the radar. The radar is thus interested in receiving an answer rather than an echo. This class of radar is known as *secondary radar*. The principle difference is that the transmission path between the transmitter and the appropriate receiver is only one way. Thus the power received at the target may be written as:

$$P_R = P_t G_t A_R / 4\pi R^2$$

For the power received at the radar from the target transmission, the subscripts need to be reversed in the sense that the transmitted part refers to the target transmitter and the received part refers to the radar receiver. A general form of the above would be:

$$P_1 = P_2 G_2 A_1 / 4\pi R^2$$

This expression allows the calculation of maximum range in either direction, given the minimum detectable signal. This is found by considering receiver noise, and probability of detection and false alarm rate requirements. The maximum range from radar to target need not be the same as the maximum range from target to radar. As it is necessary that detection takes place in both directions, one takes the shorter maximum range as the maximum range of the system overall. Although secondary radar relies upon the installation of equipment in the target, its major advantages are that the return is independent of the radar cross section of the target and that there will be no clutter to compete with, only noise.

Identification Friend or Foe (IFF)

The system described above has in many ways more affinity to a communications system than to a radar system, and it is essentially in this way that secondary radar is used. Its main use is identification of aircraft. The secondary radar's transmitted pulse acts as an interrogator, triggering the aircraft system (transponder) to reply with a coded transmission. In the case of aircraft the transmission will normally give identification, position, heading, and velocity, which is then automatically processed on to the radar screen. In military systems, this is the way in which friendly aircraft are identified, as primary radar echoes are identified as hostile by the lack of secondary radar response. In civil applications, all aircraft are friendly, and since secondary radar requires far less transmitter power, secondary radar represents the most effective way of keeping track of aircraft. Thus civil air traffic control uses this method almost exclusively. In general, IFF uses a lower transmission frequency than the main radar (typically around 800 MHz) and its transmissions are pulse synchronous with the primary radar with which it operates.

CONTINUOUS WAVE RADAR

Radar detects a target by sending r.f. energy out from a transmitting aerial, bouncing it off the target, and receiving the echo. Measurement of the Doppler frequency shift, which is present in the echo when the target range is changing, allows the radar to detect moving targets. The use of this method involves the mixing of the received signal with the transmitter leakage to produce a beat frequency. It is the detection of this frequency which indicates target presence.

The Doppler Effect

Consider Figure 7.13:
Transmitted energy is being reflected to the receiver from a moving target at

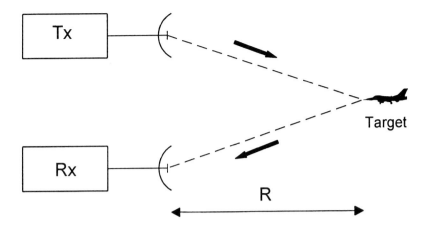

Figure 7.13 Detection of Motion

range R. Because it is moving towards the radar, it has a radial velocity with reference to the radar and this produces the change in frequency known as the Doppler shift. Although it is not proved here, this shift, f_d, is given by:

$$f_d = -2V_r/\lambda$$

Detection of the target involves detection of an echo with a Doppler shift, and analysis of target motion involves measurement of this frequency. The Doppler frequency, as may be seen from the above, is the difference frequency between the transmitted and the received signal. Use of a continuous wave radar will allow this to be obtained by mixing the two in the receiver to obtain the difference frequency. Since stationary targets, such as the ground, buildings and trees, do not yield a Doppler shift, it is relatively easy to discriminate between moving targets and the stationary background.

The actual value of the Doppler shift is easily calculable from the expression above and will have a specific value for each target. However, it is worth noting two points:

- The Doppler shift for a radar transmitting at 2cm is 100 Hz/m/sec. This means that all ground moving targets (people, tanks, etc.) produce Doppler shifts which are low enough to be heard if placed on loudspeaker or earphone. This means that detection and analysis can be done by the human ear and brain. This combination is very good at analysing sounds and equally good at analysing Doppler echoes.
- The Doppler shift for 3cm radar is 20 kHz per Mach no. This means that aircraft and missiles will tend to produce Doppler frequencies which are too high

to be treated as above, and the detection and analysis of such targets (in air defence, for example) must be done entirely electronically.

A Simple CW System

A block diagram of a simple CW system is illustrated in Figure 7.14:

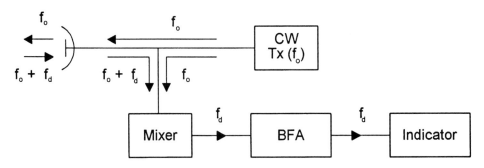

Figure 7.14 A Simple CW Radar

Signal energy returned in the echo is mixed with the transmitter leakage to give the Doppler frequency. This is amplified by a beat frequency amplifier (BFA) and fed to a suitable indicator.

The purpose of the BFA is to eliminate echoes from stationary targets and to prevent transmitter leakage from getting to the indicator. It must also provide sufficient power to feed the indicator when Doppler-shifted echoes are present. The passband of the amplifier must therefore be such that it rejects DC and passes all frequencies up to the highest expected Doppler frequency. This is shown in Figure 7.15.

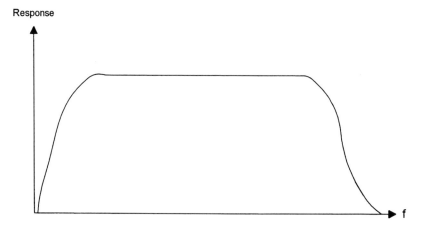

Figure 7.15 Beat Frequency Amplifier Response

The indicator may be a frequency meter (in which case it is possible to measure the Doppler frequency, and hence the range rate), or it may be a pair of earphones and the human ear. In the latter case it is only detection that is possible. However, the narrow-band characteristics of the human ear increase the signal to noise ratio, and hence the detection capability.

The disadvantages of the system are two-fold:

- There is no isolation between the transmitter output and the receiver.
- The necessary bandwidth causes noise in the receiver to be higher than one would like.

These problems are addressed below.

Receiver Isolation

Receiver isolation is necessary because high power levels reaching the receiver from the transmitter are liable to burn out parts of it. Isolation may be achieved with single-aerial systems by the use of ferrite devices, which are capable of routing transmitter power to the antenna while at the same time routing echo power to the receiver. However, the isolation achieved is not good, and this method is limited to low-power CW systems with insensitive receivers. (A radar speed trap is a good example of such a radar.)

In order to achieve high isolations, two aerials are mandatory. This method gives isolation of 80 dB and upwards. However, the use of two aerials involves the loss of capture area, as one is using only half of the available aerial aperture for reception. Also the design of two-aerial systems may well present more difficult mechanical design problems. Nevertheless, it is the only solution for high-power, sensitive CW systems.

Receiver Bandwidth

It has already been stated that the bandwidth of the BFA must be large enough to accept the full range of Doppler frequencies. This is because it is not known what Doppler frequency will arrive at the receiver at any given moment. Let us suppose, however, that we do know the frequency that will be imposed on the received signal by the target. Then we have a real chance of producing a narrow bandwidth for the receiver, thus greatly reducing receiver noise. In practice, the bandwidth of the received echo in a CW system is typically of the order of 50–100 Hz, and thus the receiver could be designed with this narrow bandwidth and still receive all the echo energy.

However, the exact value of the Doppler shift is not known, and the receiver must cover all possible values. This introduces extra noise, but also causes the loss of the exact value of the Doppler frequency, and with it the range rate of the target. Both these problems are overcome by the use of a Doppler filter bank following the BFA. Since the receiver energy will pass through only one filter at any one time, the narrow bandwidth is effectively restored, as is the ability to measure the range rate of the target. An example of such a filter bank is illustrated in Figure 7.16.

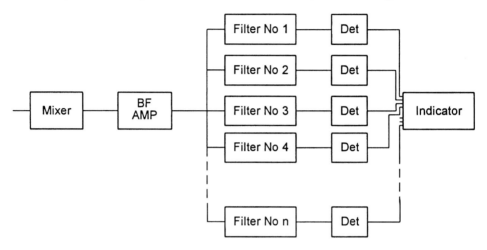

Figure 7.16 Filter Bank for Measuring Doppler Shift

The bandwidth of each filter is wide enough to accept the signal energy, but not so wide as to introduce more noise than is necessary. The centre frequencies of the filters are staggered to cover the entire range of Doppler frequencies.

An Improved CW System

Taking account of the comments regarding receiver bandwidth and isolation, an improved CW system may be constructed as illustrated in Figure 7.17.

This system is an improvement on the simple system in that it has:

- Controlled transmitter/receiver coupling.
- A filter bank for reducing noise and indicating Doppler velocity. (This bank may consist of a set of mechanical filters or, in modern equipments, be produced by signal processing using computational techniques.)

Advantages, Drawbacks and Applications of CW Sytems

The principal advantages of CW systems are their ability to measure velocities, and to detect down to zero range. The first of these properties make simple CW radar the obvious choice for Doppler sensing systems such as police speed traps,

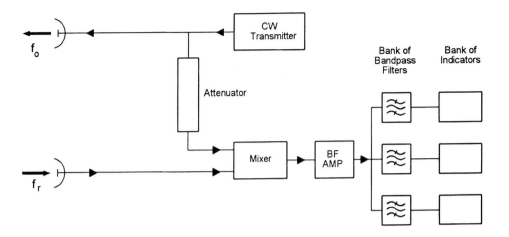

Figure 7.17 An Improved CW Radar

intruder detection, collision warning, rate of climb indication and Doppler navigation. The second of these properties makes CW the preferred choice for proximity fuses in missiles. (CW achieves this by sensing the moment when the Doppler frequency falls to zero. Assuming that the missile velocity is always higher than the target velocity, this can only occur as the missile reaches its point of closest approach to its target. This is the obvious moment to go bang!)

The major disadvantages of CW systems are the complexities involved in dealing with multiple targets and the shorter detection range that is generally achieved in practice. (Although in principle pulse and CW radars have the same detection performance, in practice transmitter leakage limits the transmitter power of the CW system more than component breakdown does in a pulse system.) Pulse systems operate best, therefore, in situations where multiple targets are likely to occur, and in situations where long detection is required. Obvious examples are search, surveillance, mapping and track-while-scan.

PULSE DOPPLER RADARS AND MTI RADARS

The previous section described CW radar and showed that it has the ability to detect moving targets in the presence of stationary clutter. Discrimination of a small target against a large clutter background can thus be achieved by using this type of radar. However, in practice CW radar is not always the answer.

Limitations of CW Radar

For surveillance of such places as the battlefield, we require a radar that is capable of more than merely detecting targets in the presence of overwhelming clutter returns; it must also be capable of detecting at large ranges. In other words it must be sensitive. Unfortunately, a CW radar is limited in sensitivity by transmitter leakage, and to get even a moderate performance separate aerials for transmission and reception are necessary. Unfortunately, separate aerials are frequently not practicable. Antenna dimensions are normally constrained to a certain size, and Figure 7.18 shows the effect of putting two antennas (as opposed to a single one) within that set size.

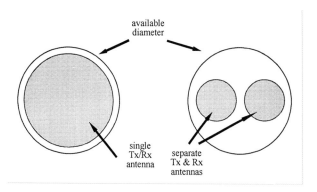

Figure 7.18 CW Places Constraints on Antenna Size

Aerial gain on transmission and capture area on reception are each reduced by a factor of four. This halves the detection range of the radar as compared with a single aerial system. Consequently designers are forced back to the use of pulse radar. This, however, has problems of its own in the area of Doppler ambiguity. These are now addressed.

Pulse Radar and Doppler Ambiguity

A pulse radar has a transmission spectrum of the form illustrated in Figure 7.19, and may be seen to consist of a line spectrum of spacing equal to f_r.

The received spectrum is shown in Figure 7.20.

It may be seen that each transmitted frequency has struck the target, and been Doppler-shifted, giving a whole set of echoes, one for each transmitted frequency. Clutter has also been struck by each transmitted frequency and been returned without a Doppler shift. This differs from the CW received spectrum only in that the clutter echo and target echo are repeated at intervals f_r. This apparently simple difference has a number of important implications:

- *Clutter.* Clutter repeats every f_r, coinciding with the transmitted frequencies. Clearly any target Doppler frequency which coincides with one of these repetitions will be masked by it, just as effectively as when clutter and target have

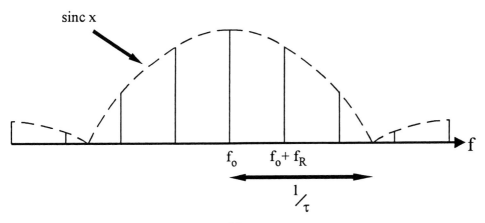

Figure 7.19 Pulse Doppler – Transmitted Spectrum

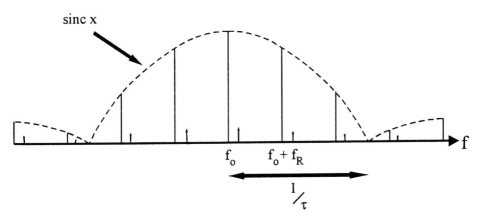

Figure 7.20 Pulse Doppler – Received Spectrum

identical (zero) Doppler frequencies. Thus there are a number of evenly-spaced Doppler frequencies where the target has to compete with the clutter echo. This problem is known as *velocity blanking*, or velocity blindness, and can be serious, as it allows a target to approach at a blind velocity right down to zero range and never be detected. It is illustrated in Figure 7.21.

Figure 7.21 Velocity Blanking

- *Target return.* The target return also repeats every f_r. This leads to the difficulty that it is not easy to tell which target Doppler frequency 'belongs' to which transmission line. This leads directly to Doppler frequency ambiguity, as obviously the measured Doppler frequency would depend on the 'guess' made. This problem is known as *velocity ambiguity*. It is illustrated in Figure 7.22.

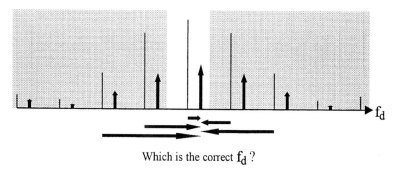

Which is the correct f_d ?

Figure 7.22 Velocity Ambiguity

PRF Constraints in Pulse Doppler

An obvious solution to the above difficulties is to use a PRF that is at least twice as large as the maximum anticipated Doppler frequency. This will ensure that the target Doppler frequency is never masked by repetitions of clutter return. It will also remove Doppler frequency ambiguities, as any target return can be safely associated with the nearest transmission line. This situation is illustrated in Figure 7.23.

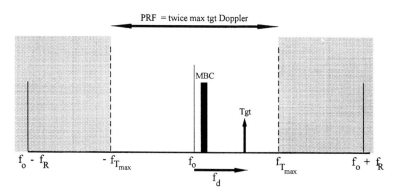

Figure 7.23 Use of High PRF to resolve Velocity Ambiguity

(The same result is obtained by considering pulse Doppler to be a sampled CW system; in this case unambiguous frequency measurement can be obtained if and only if sampling takes place at at least twice the highest frequency expected.) The radar can now use a filter bank approach for measuring Doppler, and since it is a pulse radar, it can obtain the range from echo times.

Limitation of Maximum Unambiguous Range in Pulse Doppler Radars

Constraining the PRF of the radar to greater than some minimum value may lead to problems with range ambiguity, as high PRFs produce low maximum ambiguous ranges. Whether this is a problem in practice or not depends on the radar's required role:

- *A 15 GHz (2cm) ground-based battlefield surveillance radar* might be trying to detect targets travelling at 30 m/s. At 15 GHz, this leads to a maximum expected Doppler frequency of 3 kHz. In order to avoid velocity blindness and velocity ambiguity, therefore, the PRF must be at least twice as high as this, i.e., 6 kHz. This PRF gives a value of R_{mu} of 30 km. This is beyond the maximum detection range of such radars, and thus this type of radar can be designed to be unambiguous in both velocity and range at the same time. Velocity blindness and eclipsing (an echo returning to the radar during a subsequent pulse, when the receiver is off) are consequently not problems either.
- *A 10 GHz air defence radar*, on the other hand would be trying to detect targets travelling as fast as Mach 2. Thus it will encounter Doppler frequencies as high as 40 kHz. This means that avoidance of velocity ambiguity would require PRFs above 80 kHz. Range ambiguity now commences at less than 4 km. This is clearly operationally untenable in a radar which is required more than anything else to be able to measure target range. Hence it is clearly impossible to produce a radar with single PRF which will not suffer ambiguity (and blindness) either in range or in velocity.

These two examples show that problems involved in using pulsed radar to measure velocity as well as range vary entirely on their role. Battlefield Surveillance Radars (BSRs) may be designed this way, and these radars are generally single PRF pulse Doppler radars. AD radars, on the other hand, cannot operate in this way, and another method must be employed to remove stationary clutter.

Moving Target Indication

The above discussion has dealt with the measurement of motion in pulse radars. In practice, however, many radars (AD radars among them) are not especially concerned with the measurement of velocity. Their value lies in discriminating moving targets from stationary ones. As a result, there is no interest in *measuring* Doppler, only in rejecting zero values of Doppler (a process known as *moving target indication*). Since there is no attempt to measure Doppler, it follows that the presence of Doppler ambiguity is not a problem, and the radar is happy to operate at low values of PRF.

Doppler blindness still exists, however. This is because the clutter return repeats itself at frequency intervals of PRF and consequently must be removed along with any targets with Doppler frequencies that coincide with these repetitions. The values of the resulting blind speeds can be operationally embarrassing, as they tend to be in the region of practical aircraft velocities. For instance, a 3 GHz (10cm) air defence radar with a PRF of 500 pps has a first blind speed of only 25 m/s. MTI radars get round this problem by varying the PRF. This varies the blind speeds, with the result that any target which is blind at one PRF becomes visible at a different one.

TRACKING RADAR

The purpose of directing a radar beam on to a target is usually to measure some parameter of that target, such as range, velocity or bearing. Once measured, a further requirement may be to monitor automatically the relevant parameters for that target on a continuous basis. This automatic monitoring function is known as *tracking*, and radars that perform in this way are known as *tracking radars*. The information obtained from such radars may be used for a number of purposes. However, there are two major areas of interest, and these produce two types of tracking radar.

- *Single target trackers*. Active radar homing in missiles is achieved by using a tracking radar in the nose of the missile and steering the missile towards the victim by supplying a continuous readout of the victim's position to the missile guidance circuits. Such a tracking radar observes only one target at a time and would be confused by multiple target capability. Thus it is designed as a single target tracker, which stares continuously at the target and gives unbroken target data.
- *Multiple target trackers*. Surveillance and acquisition radars scan the sky looking for possible hostile targets. The ability to keep an eye on a number of targets simultaneously and to be able to feed parameters of any required target to an appropriate missile system is clearly an asset. The same multi-track capability would be useful in airborne early warning and air traffic control. Radars that perform in this way are tracking while they scan, updating target data on each pass of the aerial beam through the target. These systems are fre-

quently known as *track-while-scan* (TWS) radars, for obvious reasons.

The two types of radar mentioned above are fundamentally different in their principles of operation, and must therefore be discussed separately. This account will deal only with single target tracking, but it is as well to be aware that TWS systems exist.

Angle Tracking in Single Target Tracker

In order to monitor the direction of a designated target, it is necessary only to keep the aerial pointing direct at the target. Knowledge of the pointing direction of the aerial then naturally gives knowledge of the target direction. In order to keep a single target tracker staring at the designated target automatically it is necessary to have a control system that keeps the aerial beam pointing at it regardless of the target motion. An apparently obvious method for doing this is to utilise the idea that the radar will get maximum received power when the target is in the beam centre. Circuitry designed to monitor any fall-off in received signal strength could be used to produce a signal to a servo-motor which would steer the aerial to keep up with target motion. There are three difficulties with this method:

- The radar will have no idea in which direction the target has moved, and therefore no idea in which way to drive the aerial.
- As the target moves away from the beam centre, the received power changes only very slowly at first. Thus the system is rather insensitive to aerial pointing errors.
- Real variations in target echo power caused by scintillation will be interpreted as target motion.

All these difficulties may be removed by the use of two overlapping beams, as illustrated in Figure 7.24.

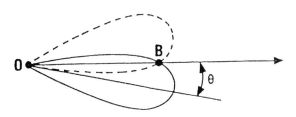

Figure 7.24 Angle Tracking – Use of Two Beams

In this diagram, if the target is situated on the centre line OB, echo powers received by the two beams will be the same. (In tracking radars, the aerial centre line is known as the aerial boresight.) However, any target movement into, say, the bottom beam will reduce the return to the top beam, and increase that to the bottom beam. There is now a difference between the two and this may be used to generate an error signal. This signal can be used to cause a servo-motor to drive the aerial in the correct direction to keep the aerial boresight pointing at the target. Figure 7.25 shows the two beam patterns in Cartesian rather than polar form, and Figure 7.26 shows the difference between the two returns as a function of pointing error.

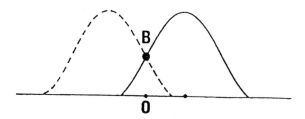

Figure 7.25 Use of Two Beams – Cartesian Representation

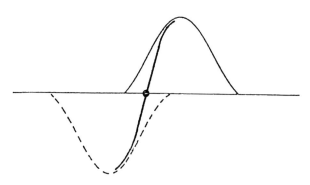

Figure 7.26 Production of Error Signal

It can be seen that:

- The difference signal is a sign which is dependent on the sense of the pointing error. Translated into a driving voltage for the servo-motor, this means that the antenna can always be driven in the correct direction to reduce the pointing error to zero.
- The difference signal increases rapidly as the pointing error grows from zero. Thus the system is sensitive to such errors. Indeed, practical systems are able to maintain correct pointing typically to within one-hundredth of a beamwidth.

- If the target is on the boresight, then real changes in target return affect each beam equally, and hence the difference signal remains zero.

Thus all three of the problems mentioned above have been solved by the use of two beams. It should, however, be pointed out that the third one does involve the assumption that the two beams are operating simultaneously, rather than sequentially.

Actually both arrangements exist, with simultaneous operation being superior in that it is insensitive to target scintillation. Sequential operation may be very sensitive to scintillation and as such is an inferior approach. As already stated, both arrangements exist in practical equipments and thus both will be discussed below.

Amplitude Comparison Monopulse Angle Tracking

A radar that utilises the simultaneous arrangement mentioned above is termed a *monopulse* radar. This is because it gains all its pointing information from a single pulse of the transmitter. The method is to use an aerial which forms two independent beams. The transmitter pulse is fed into both. On reception, the two beams receive independently, and their returns are compared in amplitude to produce the error signal. In practice, two beams are only enough to track in one dimension (elevation or azimuth). To obtain two-dimensional tracking (elevation and azimuth) more beams are required, with four being the usual number. Figure 7.27 illustrates this in terms of four beam footprints in the sky.

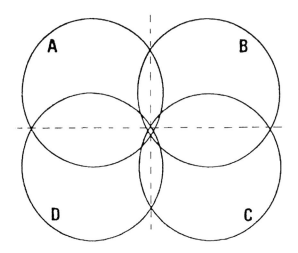

Figure 7.27 Amplitude Comparison Monopulse – Four Beams

Comparison between either top beam and either bottom beam will allow the

target to be tracked on to the horizontal centre line. Comparison between either left-hand beam with either right-hand beam will allow the target to be tracked on to the vertical centre line. To track to both requires two error signals and two servos. If these are present then the target will be tracked on to the boresight of the aerial system. In practice, comparison takes place between the sums of top and bottom, and the sums of left and right.

The circuitry required to perform the tasks above is illustrated in Figure 7.28.

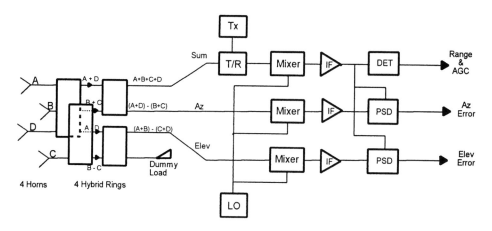

Figure 7.28 Amplitude Comparison Monopulse – Receiver Circuitry

The production of the two difference signals is implemented by the use of hybrid rings and two independent receiver channels. A third receiver channel operates on the sum of all four beams. This channel has three functions.

- It gives the strongest possible signal to feed to the detection circuitry (as in an ordinary pulse radar).
- It gives a reference phase with which the difference signals can be compared in order to obtain sense information for the error signals.
- It provides an automatic gain control (AGC) for all three channels, thus ensuring that the final error signals depend only on pointing error, and not also on signal strength. (Within certain obvious practical constraints, this allows tracking radars to have the same characteristics for all targets, regardless of range.)

It is important that all three channels have the same characteristics in phase and amplitude. Failure to achieve this, particularly in phase, results in the tracking being less sensitive. This was hard to achieve in the days of valves, and consequently monopulse techniques were introduced relatively late in the history of tracking radar.

Phase Comparison Monopulse Angle Tracking

Amplitude comparison monopulse is the most common form of monopulse tracking. However, it is not this form that has the potential for greatest accuracy. This is supplied by *phase comparison monopulse*. The method uses two aerials separated by a distance *d*, as illustrated in Figure 7.29.

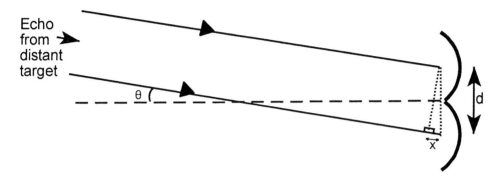

Figure 7.29 Phase Comparison Monopulse – Principle

One of the aerials only is used on transmit. On receive, however, both aerials accept the return, and the phase difference between the two is used to produce an error signal. If the target is on the tracking boresight, the phase difference will be zero. If the target is θ off the centre line, there will be an extra distance, $x = d \sin\theta$, to one of the aerials. This produces a phase difference between the two aerials of:

$$\phi = (2\pi d \sin\theta)/\lambda$$

For small angles off boresight, this gives the phase difference proportional to the pointing error. A block diagram of the phase comparison receiver is shown in Figure 7.30, where it can be seen that the error signal can be made proportional to pointing error by the use of a phase sensitive detector (PSD).

(Note that to get zero output for zero phase difference, it is necessary to have a 90° phase difference built into one or other receiver channel.)

This system is much simpler than amplitude comparison monopulse and can be made as sensitive as one wishes, simply by picking an appropriate spacing for the two aerials. (Wide spacings will give good sensitivity to pointing errors.) However, they will also give grating lobes, and require a large aperture to fit into. Furthermore, phase comparison monopulse, being a two-aerial system, does not make the best use of the available aperture. When used in elevation it is also the victim of phase distortions in situations where ground reflections are a problem.

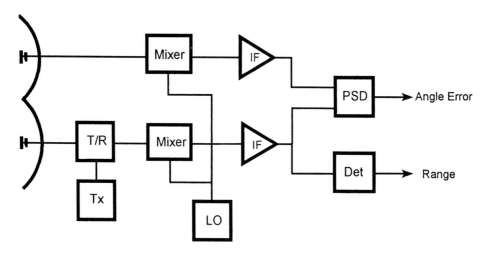

Figure 7.30 Phase Comparison Monopulse – Receiver Circuitry

Thus in ground-based tracking systems, the system is limited to use in azimuth, and fits better into the world of interferometric direction finding than single-target tracking. However, in airborne situations one of the first monopulse tracking radars (that of the English Electric *Lightning*) was phase comparison in azimuth, with amplitude comparison being used in elevation. Also, missile homing heads are frequently phase-comparison systems in order to produce simpler receivers. This is particularly true at millimetric wavelengths, where good separation in wavelengths may be obtained in quite small physical apertures.

Conical Scan Angle Tracking

Monopulse systems are the best single-target trackers. However, their receiver processing is not simple to engineer, and consequently a much simpler system, known as *conical scan*, was implemented in early tracking radars. This system exists in equipment still in service, and consequently it is necessary to discuss its principles of operation. However, it must be emphasised that the performance of conical scan is worse than that of monopulse in all areas of operation.

Figure 7.31 shows the principle of the scan pattern.

An off-set feed rotates about the boresight, producing a scan pattern in which the beam describes a circle in the sky. This is illustrated in Figure 7.32. with a target (A) at the centre of the scan pattern (i.e., on the tracking boresight).

As the beam is scanned it stays a constant angular distance from this target at all parts of the scan pattern. Thus the received echoes will be constant, as shown in Figure 7.33.

If the target were to drift away from the centre of the scan pattern to B, say,

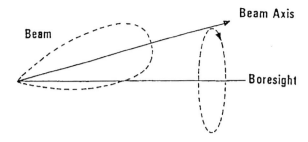

Figure 7.31 Conical Scan Tracking

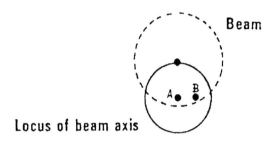

Figure 7.32 Conical Scan Tracking – Scan Pattern

Figure 7.33 Received Signal Strength with No Pointing Error

then a pointing error would be present. However, because the beam is now passing closer to the target at some times than it ʼs at others, the received echoes will be amplitude-modulated at scanning frequency (as shown in Figure 7.34).

Figure 7.34 Received Signal Strength with Pointing Error

The presence of the amplitude modulation indicates a pointing error, and all that is now required is to turn this modulation into azimuth and elevation error voltages to drive the centre of the scan pattern back on to the target. The block diagram of the receiver is shown in Figure 7.35, and it can be seen that the receiver detects down to baseband, where one is left with a sinusoid at scanning frequency, being sampled at the PRF.

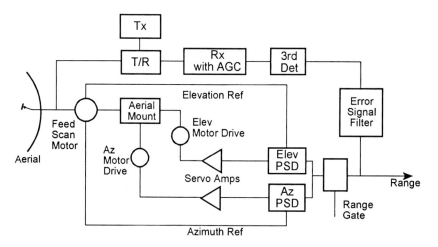

Figure 7.35 Conical Scan – Receiver Circuitry

The error signal filter smooths this pulsed waveform into a continuous sinusoid. This is now mixed with two phase quadrature waveforms derived from the aerial scan to produce error voltages for the azimuth and elevation servos.

Typical scanning frequencies are in the region of 30 Hz, and thus typical PRFs are above 120 Hz. The system suffers from scintillation (being a sequential system), but not as seriously as might be expected. The servo bandwidth is typically of the order of 2–5 Hz, and only scintillation within this bandwidth centred on the scanning frequency will get to the servo motors. However, the system is extremely easy to deceive and this is its major operational drawback.

Range Tracking in Single-Target Trackers

The main purpose of range tracking is to provide continuous range information for a selected target. It uses a range gate method to achieve this, allowing the receiver to be on only at the time when the designated target echo is expected. Automatic tracking is achieved by the use of an early gate and a late gate. Figure 7.36 shows the scheme.

If the switchover between these two gates is at the exact centre of the return pulse, then each gate will get the same received echo energy, and a difference circuit will give an output of zero. Knowing the time of switchover thus gives the correct echo time of the target, and hence its range. If the range changes, however, the switchover will no longer be in the centre of the returned energy distribution, and the difference circuit will give a non-zero output. This may be used as an error signal and will change the timing of the gates, bringing the switchover back to the pulse centre. Once again, the difference signal is signed, and thus the timing may be made earlier or later, depending on which gate is accepting the greatest pulse energy.

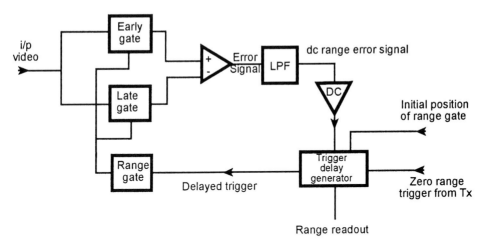

Figure 7.36 Range Tracking

Velocity Tracking in Single Target Trackers

Velocity tracking operates on similar principles to range tracking. However, instead of controlling two range gates, one controls the frequency of the local oscillator. Figure 7.37 illustrates the principle.

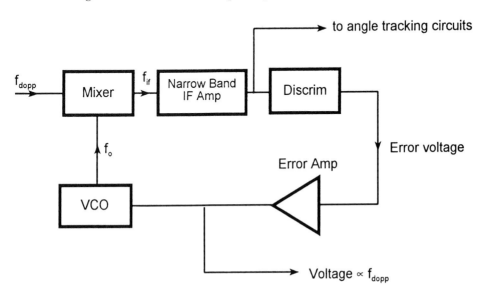

Figure 7.37 Velocity Tracking

The mixer is designed to bring the received frequency down to a predetermined intermediate frequency (IF). Any Doppler frequency present will cause a frequency error. The discriminator measures departure from IF, and generates a voltage which is proportional to this departure. This voltage is used to change the local oscillator frequency in such a way as to bring the mixer output back to IF. The size of the error voltage is a measure of the Doppler frequency. Thus velocity tracking is achieved. It is worth noting that this system has two other effects which improve the performance of the radar:

- it provides a velocity gate in the form of a narrow band IF amplifier, and consequently competing targets of different radial velocities are eliminated;
- filtering in the IF eliminates noise, and thus the signal-to-noise ratio is improved.

BATTLEFIELD SURVEILLANCE RADAR

There are two important applications for radar in battlefield surveillance:

- short-range surveillance and target acquisition using short-range ground-based radars.
- longer-range surveillance out to further than 100km. This need can be met by an airborne or spaceborne radar.

These applications are outlined below.

Ground-Based Battlefield Surveillance Radar

The requirement for ground-based battlefield surveillance radars (BSRs) is for the detection and location of:

- ground-based targets at all ranges out to the local horizon, and
- helicopters and RPVs within line-of-sight.

These tasks can also be carried out by optical and IR surveillance systems. However, the long-range, all-weather ability of radar allows operation in the presence of poor weather conditions and battlefield obscuration, conditions which could defeat optical or IR systems even at short range. Radar also readily offers continuous wide-area coverage, together with the possibility of automatic alarm, thus giving freedom from watch fatigue under certain conditions. Targets of interest include personnel, static and moving vehicles, helicopters, RPVs and fall of shot. The primary technical problems encountered with these kinds of target are the large clutter return from the stationary ground and the need to classify target type. Both these requirements can be addressed by using Doppler processing. The additional need to locate the target in range as well as bearing means that the use of pulse Doppler is to be preferred.

The frequency of operation of a BSR is determined by the need for:

- detection of all target types, in all weathers, out to the maximum required detection range (typically 6–12km);
- good resolution in range and in angle; and
- a radar equipment that is physically small.

The resolution and size requirements are best achieved by using as high a transmission frequency as possible. However, frequencies above about 20 GHz are unsatisfactory because weather attenuation and limited transmitter power compromise the required detection performance. Thus the transmission frequency usually employed lies between 10 and 20 GHz. PRF is determined by the maximum range requirement and by the maximum expected target velocity. Typically, unambiguous range and velocity measurement can be achieved in the region of 4–10 kHz. Pulse length and antenna size are dictated by the required range and angle resolutions. For example, a range resolution of 25m requires a pulse length of no more than 0.16µS. Similarly, if an angular resolution of 50m at 1km is required, then the antenna beamwidth must be no more than 50 mil (3 degrees). This can be obtained with an antenna size of 0.6m at 10 GHz, or one of 0.3m at 20 GHz. A large antenna would, of course, provide better angular resolution, but at the expense of easy portability.

Figure 7.38 shows the layout and Figure 7.39 shows a photograph of a typical BSR and highlights several important features. The narrow antenna beamwidth means that a rigid tripod is necessary, together with servos to handle the required sector and give some degree of elevation control. The conventional radar hardware is supplemented by digital signal processing to give enhanced clutter rejection and signal detection, and to control the radar operation and data display. The radar data is presented to the operator in several ways. Headphones allow him to listen to the Doppler signature of specific targets and hence classify them. Automatic alarm of target presence in critical point locations, together with a wide display and data readout, can also be incorporated in to the operator unit. A typical display unit is shown in Figure 7.40 and this can be remoted from the radar head.

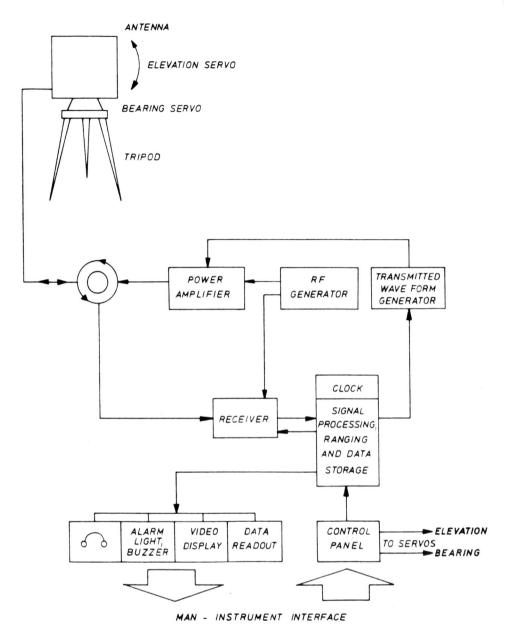

Figure 7.38 Block Diagram of a Typical Pulse Doppler Battlefield Surveillance Radar

Figure 7.39 Man Portable Surveillance and Target Acquisition Radar (MSTAR) (*photo courtesy of Racal Radar Defence Systems Ltd*)

Figure 7.40 MSTAR Display and Control Unit (*photo courtesy of Racal Radar Defence Systems Ltd*)

Airborne Battlefield Surveillance Radar

Surveillance and target acquisition at ranges in excess of 100km and in all weathers calls for radars mounted in airborne platforms. Several types of platform have been considered to meet this need, including tethered platforms such as balloons, but manned aircraft are primarily used. Figure 7.41 shows how the airborne radar can be used to view an area beyond the front line. The aircraft can either be close to the front line at low altitude or, where this is considered too vulnerable, further back at higher altitude. The radar may be a conventional MTI type in which non-static ground targets can be detected against the clutter background by virtue of their motion over the stationary ground. Alternatively, a form of imaging radar known as synthetic aperture radar (SAR) can be used to give a radar picture of the area in which both stationary and moving targets are seen and in which details of the scene stand out as a result of differences in their radar reflectivity. Figure 7.42 shows a SAR image alongside a map of the same area. Roads and fields can be clearly seen. Superimposed on the SAR image are

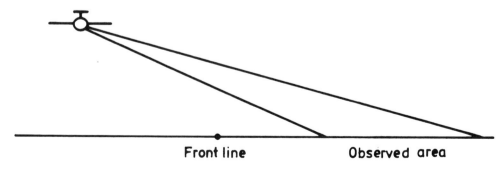

Figure 7.41 Airborne Battlefield Surveillance Concept

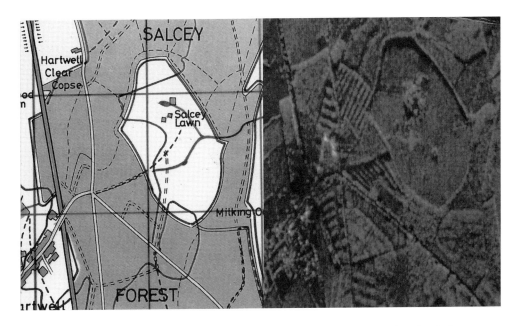

Figure 7.42 Synthetic Aperture Radar Image (*photo courtesy of Racal Radar Defence Systems Ltd*)

dots representing moving targets. These dots with no background image are what would be seen with a MTI radar. The main advantage of the MTI display is the ease of interpretation. This is of particular importance when surveillance over large areas is required.

The key technical parameters for these two types of radar are resolution and measurement accuracy. Figure 7.43 shows the geometry for determining resolutions. The range resolution d_{el} is given by:

$$d_{el} = c\tau/(2 \cos \theta)$$

where θ is the look-down angle of the radar beam. Short pulses will in many cases give a satisfactory range resolution (for example, $\tau = 0.1$ μS gives d_{el} of the order of 15m). If better range resolution is required, pulse compression can be employed. This is capable of giving range resolutions of the order of one metre. The cross-range resolution d_{az} given by

$$d_{az} = R\theta_B$$

where θ_B is the azimuth beamwidth of the radar, and R is the range. For example, using a range of 100km and a 1m sized antenna operating at 10 GHz, the cross-range resolution is 3km. This is clearly inadequate, as it means that

201

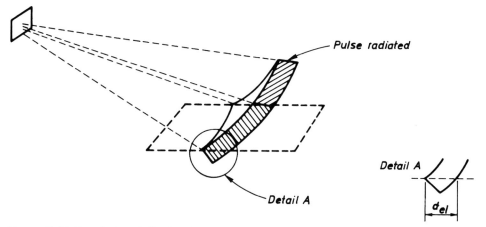

Figure 7.43 Resolution Cell of Pulse Airborne Radar

objects on the ground have to be separated by more than 3km to be distinguished from each other. The solution to this problem differs in the two types of radar.

MTI radars. These rely on the fact that the elimination of all stationary clutter leaves relatively few targets to process. The use of high range resolution allows each of these targets to be individually resolved. Once this has been done, the split-beam technique used in monopulse radars can be employed to produce azimuth measurements of each target, to an accuracy of between 0.1 and 0.01 of a beamwidth. At 100km this gives a cross-range measurement accuracy that may be as good as 30m. This is good enough to provide useful information about enemy activity.

Synthetic aperture radars. To achieve true imaging resolutions at long ranges, the use of a very large antenna is required, and this is the technique employed in SAR, where signal processing is used to synthesise an extremely long antenna, with a correspondingly small beamwidth. The basic action is illustrated in Figure 7.44. The aircraft with its sideways-looking radar flies a distance L. At the start at time $t = t_1$, the object P is just in the edge of the radar antenna's beam. At the end, at time $t = t_2$, the object is just leaving the other side of the beam. During the time $t_1 - t_2$ the returns from the range corresponding to the target P are processed to produce the same output as would be received from a real antenna of length $2L$. The beamwidth, θ_s, of this synthesised antenna is given by:

$$\theta_s = \lambda / 2L \text{ radians}$$

However, Figure 7.44 shows that L is given by

$$L = R\theta_B,$$

and since the beamwidth of the real antenna is given in terms of its size, D, by

$$\theta_B = \lambda/D \text{ radians,}$$

the beamwidth of the synthesised antenna can be expressed in terms of the size of the real antenna as:

$$\theta_s = D/2R$$

Since the cross-range resolution of any antenna at range R equals $R\theta$, the value for the synthesised antenna is $R\theta_s$. This gives a cross-range resolution, d_{az}, for the synthesised antenna as:

$$d_{az} = D/2$$

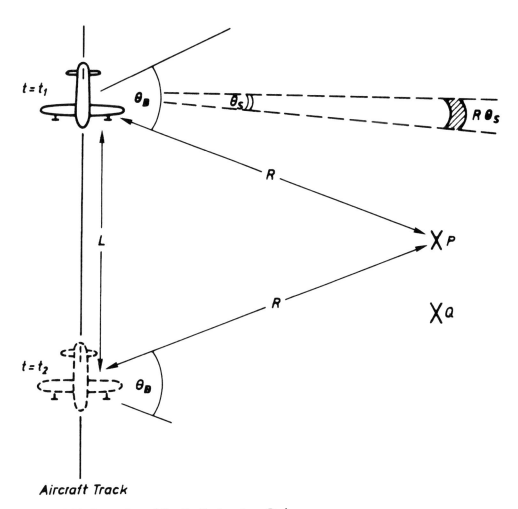

Aircraft Track

Figure 7.44 Operation of Synthetic Aperture Radar

Thus for the 1m antenna used above, d_{az} = 0.5m. It should be noted that, in theory at least, this resolution is independent of range and improves as the real antenna gets smaller. To achieve these very high resolutions in practice requires a very steady aircraft track, very stable radar oscillators and processing that corrects the small but significant change in range of the target as the aircraft flies past, a technique known as focusing. SAR is highly processing-intensive, and the better the required resolution the greater the amount of processing required. In most SARs this results in resolutions being limited by present-day processing capability, and so practical imaging resolutions may not match what is possible in theory. Resolutions of the order of 10m are manageable, however, and this allows long-range reconnaissance of military formations deep within enemy territory. Further aspects that affect the use of such airborne imaging include:

- the significant shadowing by undulating terrain that low-angle radars experience;
- the problem of interpretation of radar imagery.

The problem highlights the similarity of use between radar and optical imagery. Both provide reconnaissance information and both must be examined in detail by specialists skilled in using the techniques of photo-interpretation.

Both MTI and SAR provide useful reconnaissance information, and in practice the two techniques complement each other to give a good picture of military activity deep in enemy territory.

WEAPON-LOCATING RADAR

Radars for locating mortars were first used in Italy in 1944 and are now in service throughout the world. The location of guns and rocket launchers is a difficult radar requirement because of the small size of the projectile and the large number of targets that the radar needs to resolve. In practice, the radar must have a high output power and a large antenna if it is to detect and accurately track such small targets. Two approaches to the problem have been employed:

Systems using mechanically steered antennas. Figure 7.45 shows this method of using radar to locate a mortar. Here the radar beam is swept mechanically backwards and forwards across the horizon at a low elevation. The Figure shows the beam at one instant during this scan. When the mortar is fired its position P_1 is measured as it passes through the beam. The antenna reflector feed is then tilted so that the swept beam moves to an elevated position and a second point P_2 in the trajectory is measured. Points P_1 and P_2, together with the time between measurements and knowledge of the ground height in the mortar area, allow the radar computer to calculate the mortar location. This two-point location method

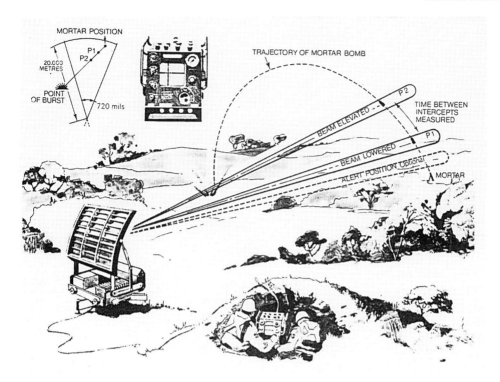

Figure 7.45 Mortar Locating Radar – The Two Point Intercept Method

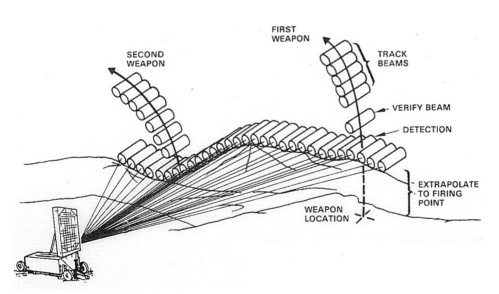

Figure 7.46 Weapon Location Using Phased Array Radar

radar is relatively simple to design and construct but has no capability against guns or rockets.

Systems using phased arrays. Improved technology, particularly in the antenna field, has enabled the threat from guns and rockets to be addressed by using the method of operation shown in Figure 7.46. Here a phased array antenna, which is capable of electronic beam-steering, allows rapid movement of a single beam and independent control of multiple beams. In operation the radar measures the horizon contour and scans a beam along it to form an electronic fence. When this fence is broken by a projectile another beam is used to verify, first, the target detection and, if successful, to track the target for a sufficient time to allow an accurate extrapolation back to the firing point. Other projectiles may also be tracked while this is happening. Figure 7.47 shows AN/TPQ-37, an example of a phased array gun and rocket locating radar. The high accuracy and long range at which projectiles must be detected and tracked lead to a very large radar installation which is hard to conceal, both physically and electronically. Because a phased array points its beam using electronic circuitry rather than by physically moving the antenna, movement of the radar beam is inertialess. This allows it to be switched from one direction to another in microseconds, apparently giving simultaneous coverage of large angular sectors and simultaneous tracking of multiple targets.

AIR DEFENCE RADAR

An air defence system is required to *detect* and *destroy* hostile air threats before they are able to carry out their missions. The role of radar within such a system is thus essentially twofold:

- to give timely warning of potential air threats entering friendly air space, and if possible aid in their identification;
- to monitor targets that have been established as hostile so that this information can be used to help in the destruction of the threat.

Thus two primary classifications exist:

- search radar intended to detect and assess incoming threats;
- tracking radars intended to provide guidance information to help the weapon find its target.

The precise design of an air defence system depends on its required role. For the radars used within such a system, the critical parameter is required detection range, and this is the classification used below.

Figure 7.47 US Firefinder AN/TPQ–37 Gun Locating Radar (*photo courtesy of Hughes Aircraft Company*)

Strategic Systems

Strategic systems are part of continental defence. Ballistic missiles are typical targets. The aim of the system is the detection and destruction of these weapons. However, ballistic missiles are difficult to destroy and so these systems have tended to concentrate on the detection and prediction of missile impact points. Ballistic missiles must be detected at ranges of thousands of kilometres. In addition, they have a low RCS. This forces the radar to have high transmitter power and a large antenna. It must also use a low transmitter frequency to minimise atmospheric attenuation. All three requirements lead to a large and expensive system. An example of such a system is the ballistic missile radar PAVE PAWS, illustrated in Figure 7.48. It can be seen that the radar has a large phased-array antenna (30m diameter), which is capable of very high output powers. The transmission frequency is in the low UHF. Electronic beam-steering is used to enable the radar to detect and track multiple targets simultaneously, with a view to determining launch and impact points for each weapon.

Figure 7.48 PAVE PAWS Radar (*photo courtesy of Raytheon Company*)

Long-Range Systems

Long-range air defence systems are normally part of a national, or large-area, defence. Their primary function is the detection and destruction of incoming enemy aircraft. Destruction is usually carried out by an airborne interceptor, which uses its own radar to home in on its target, and its own weapon system to destroy it. The role of the air defence radar is therefore limited to timely initial detection,

Figure 7.49 Martello Long-Range Air Defence Radar (*photo courtesy of GEC-Marconi Radar and Defence Systems Ltd*)

and some assistance with the early stages of intercept. These functions can be carried out by a long-range surveillance radar. *Martello*, a ground-based radar of this type, is illustrated in Figure 7.49. This radar operates in D band, giving the required detection range of 400–500km. The radar is transportable on a number of trailers, so that its location cannot be pre-targeted by any potential enemy.

Ground-based microwave surveillance radars cannot detect low-flying threats at long range, because these threats are below the horizon. An alternative approach is to place the radar on a suitable airborne platform. This extends the distance to the horizon, and allows earlier warning of approaching threats. Figure 7.50 shows an example of this in the Airborne Early Warning and Control System (known as AWACS). This system is flown high enough give an horizon distance of around 350–400km. The transmission frequency is 3 GHz, which is typical for long-range surveillance. Because the radar is carried by a moving platform and requires to have look-down capability against low-flying targets, the radar is pulse Doppler.

Figure 7.50 AWACS Radar (*photo courtesy of Raytheon Company*)

Medium-Range Systems

These systems are usually designed for area defence, and destruction of threats is carried out using a medium-range missile. Since the system covers an area, it is likely that it will need to deal with multiple threats. The radar requirements therefore include timely detection and tracking of multiple targets. An example of a radar in such a system is *Patriot*, illustrated in Figure 7.51. The phased array antenna uses electronic beam-steering. This allows the radar to search and to track simultaneously, enabling the system to engage multiple targets. The lower range requirement of the system enables a lower output power and a higher radar frequency to be used, thus allowing the employment of a radar which is smaller and hence can be made mobile. The requirement to undertake surveillance and tracking functions simultaneously is inherent in medium-range systems.

Figure 7.51 Patriot Air Defence System Radar (*photo courtesy of Raytheon Company*)

Consequently in those systems where a phased array antenna is not employed, and hence its multi-function capability is not available, the requirement is for two radars, one to perform each task.

Short-Range Systems

Here the system requirement is for point defence. The weapon employed is usually a short-range missile, but an alternative is a radar-directed gun. In either case the reduced coverage requirement and shortened engagement times result in the possibility of engaging threats one at a time. Thus the radar need search only until a target is found. It may then stop the search process and aid in the destruction process, returning to the search mode only after the engagement is over. Figures 7.52 (a) and (b) show the *Rapier* system. In its original form, the surveillance radar was used to detect an incoming target, at which point it would stop searching and acquire the target in bearing. This was then used to cue the optical system which was responsible for guiding the missile to its target. More recently, the surveillance radar is used to cue a second radar, the *Blindfire* tracking radar, on to the correct bearing. The *Blindfire* acquires the target in elevation, and from then on controls the engagement. At this point the surveillance radar

Figure 7.52 (a) Alerting Radar (*photo courtesy of British Aerospace*)

Figure 7.52 (b) Blindfire Tracking Radar (*photo courtesy of British Aerospace*)

can return to its surveillance role. The use of a high radar frequency and monopulse tracking allows the *Blindfire* approach to achieve high accuracy.

MILLIMETRIC WAVELENGTH RADARS

Radar operating at frequencies in the range 30–300 GHz (and hence having wavelengths between 10 and 1mm) are of growing importance on the battlefield, particularly in the area of terminally-guided missiles and munitions for the attack of ground targets such as tanks. This application requires high resolution coupled with some all-weather capability. Table 7.2 summarises the key properties of the possible candidates for this task.

Table 7.2

	Microwave Radar	Millimetre Wave Radar	Electro-Optic Systems
resolution	poor	fair	good
range performance	long	short	short
all-weather capability	good	fair	poor

In practice, conventional microwave radar cannot achieve the resolution necessary to separate a tank from the ground clutter surrounding it. Electro-optic systems operate satisfactorily only in fair weather. Millimetre wave systems, however, perform moderately well in both these areas. This capability, coupled with advanced target recognition techniques, enables this technology to be used in terminal homing against ground targets such as tanks. Figure 7.53 shows one possible application, the Merlin guided mortar bomb, which was designed with a millimetre wave homing seeker.

SUMMARY

Radar is an important method of surveillance and target acquisition. It combines both long-range and all-weather capabilities, but is active and has poor resolution compared with electro-optic systems. In spite of these drawbacks, its capability in the detection of small, fast targets and its ability to form images at long ranges make it the preferred solution in some of the more demanding battlefield sensor requirements. This is especially true for weapon location and long-range airborne surveillance. The wide range of other radars currently in use are also evidence of the utility and flexibility of the technique.

Radar performance can be seen as being complementary to electro-optic

Figure 7.53 Merlin Guided Mortar Bomb and Millimetre Wave Radar Seeker

equipment which has, in general, shorter range capability but much better imaging resolution. This suggests that an optimum sensor may well combine both a radar and an electro-optic device. Such combined systems have been demonstrated, although their implementation is likely to be limited by their greater cost.

The increasing demands made on radar, witnessed, for example, by the need for air defence radars to deal with many targets simultaneously, are driving equipment designers to incorporate more and more complex signal processing and more sophisticated control of phased arrays. The need for counters to electronic warfare further heightens this drive.

These factors make radar systems perhaps the most complex of all modern surveillance devices. Despite the continuing reduction in the cost of signal processing this is likely to remain true into the foreseeable future.

8

Surveillance in Depth

'I have spent all my life trying to guess what lay on the other side of the hill'

The Duke of Wellington

THE NEED

With modern weapon systems delivering longer and longer range performance, the commander now needs a greater depth of intelligence. In general, the intelligence range requirement will far exceed that of 'the other side of the hill'.

Only at the very lowest levels of command is most of this knowledge acquired by line-of-sight observations, where the need is for accurate and timely information to engage the enemy with direct-fire weapons.

At brigade level, because of the greater variety and ranges of weapons available, there is a need to plan further in advance. The type and depth of intelligence required is therefore different. The requirement includes the detection of enemy movement in depth (reinforcements and reserves), air-defence locations, headquarters and other significant tactical indications.

At even higher levels of command, greater emphasis will be placed on determining the enemy's capabilities and intentions in order to plan operations and deploy reserves. These may be indicated by the density and direction of movement of enemy elements, including forces in contact and in depth to the limit of the commander's area of intelligence interest.

This requirement demands the ability to see into dead ground and beyond the line of sight to a range determined by the presence of enemy forces that can affect the activity of the level of command concerned.

While the requirement is clear, the technology and resources required to provide adequate surveillance and target acquisition (STA) have been slow in coming into service. Although the acronym STA may be used, the requirement is better stated in terms of 'intelligence need' and 'fire support need' since these reflect more accurately the battlefield operating systems.

PERFORMANCE CHARACTERISTICS

The full requirement for depth STA systems is complex but there are certain characteristic requirements which must be fulfilled.

Resolution and Accuracy

The intelligence need is concerned with the activities of company-sized groups of specialists and larger units of armour, infantry and reserves. Although it would be useful to recognise vehicles and determine unit identities, there is no need for pinpoint accuracy, as a sufficiently faithful picture can be obtained from coarse-grade information, provided that deployment patterns can be recognised so that units may be categorised by arm or service and size. High-resolution systems are not therefore essential for the intelligence need.

In contrast it is necessary, from the fire-support point of view, to recognise the target and to know its deployment such that the appropriately-sized fire unit and ammunition may be used. This requires the type of vehicle to be recognised and consequently high-resolution systems are needed. The location of the target must also be specified to sufficient accuracy to allow first-salvo effectiveness. There is also a need to be able to carry out battlefield damage assessment, for without this there is no means to determine success or otherwise in writing down the enemy's forces before his entry into the contact battle. The requirement is further emphasised with the finite quantities of precision guided weapons available and the need to exercise fire control to maximise their effect.

Timeliness of Information

Information must be obtained in sufficient time to allow the commander to react. Quite long periods of time may be necessary to interpret the information acquired, to assess it and formulate plans, issue orders and carry out deployments. This requirement for timely information dictates the response times for systems and can also determine the range at which they must be effective. While real-time information may not be possible, delays in the acquisition and transmission of information must be minimised. As a rule of thumb, the higher the level of command the longer the delay permissible between the events taking place and the analysis of its significance. Nevertheless, all delay eats into the commander's decision time and is an inefficiency which may be exploited by a capable enemy.

Fire-support systems require real-time information on the presence of a target and the ability to track it so that the inevitable delay in bringing weapons to bear does not allow the target to escape.

Coverage

Intelligence systems need to cover large areas and to update the acquired data with a frequency dependent on the level of command and the characteristics of the information they are collating.

Fire-support STA assets need to be directed to an area commensurate with the weapon effect area they are supporting and they must also be capable of loitering and battlefield damage assessment.

Range

The range requirement is complex and is much dependent upon the level of command at which the surveillance asset is to be deployed. The key determinant is the time it will take for the formation under surveillance to enter the area of influence of the commander. At divisional level it is a fair assumption that a total of five hours is required to assess combat intelligence, formulate a plan, issue orders, move and deploy a reserve brigade. On a conservative assumption, giving the enemy a rate of advance of 10kph, then the minimum range of a division's surveillance assets should be approximately 50km. A corps might require surveillance capability up to 150 to 250km.

For fire-support roles the range of the STA assets must be greater than that of the weapon delivery system to allow time for the decision-making process to take place. For example, to acquire targets for MLRS requires an STA asset range of approximately 40km.

Acquisition Rates

Systems with a high acquisition rate are needed to gather the quantities of data necessary if the area to be covered is to be updated with sufficient frequency to provide an accurate intelligence picture. For fire-support purposes, however, a lower rate is acceptable for this is set by the number of depth fire assets available and their rate of fire or sortie rate.

Survivability

Since depth STA systems must, in general, either operate over enemy territory or look deep into it, they are inevitably more prone to detection and hence are vulnerable. Survivability is therefore a critical factor in system performance and, indeed, a controversial one since it is difficult to determine in precise terms what the probability of survival of a system will be. It is not difficult to determine how a system could be located and neutralised. It is, however, not possible to assess accurately how great a threat the enemy will consider it to be and hence what resources he will allocate to defeating it. While a system may look vulnerable from a technical point of view, it may be that a family of systems exploiting different technologies and deployed in quantity will pose such a formidable capability to be overcome that sufficient will survive an attack to be effective.

From these performance requirements it is difficult to reconcile the characteristics of a system that can fulfil both the intelligence and the fire-support role. Furthermore, even if it were so, the problems of prioritising what is bound to be a scarce resource would require considerable thought.

DEPTH STA SYSTEMS

Surveillance from Space

The ability of a satellite to be deployed without the assistance, or acquiesence, of the countries over which it passes is one of its strongest assets. The Gulf War was the first one in which satellite surveillance had an almost decisive role. This was because of a lack of reconnaissance capability in theatre, and much of the tactical work normally done by aircraft had to be done by satellites that were used specifically for that purpose.

This was made possible by the US TENCAP (Tactical Exploitation of National Capabilities) begun in the 1970s to use national sensor systems, the outputs of which are closely held in Washington for tactical support, with the analysis being sent forward to commanders in the field. Without tactical systems the war could not have been fought so successfully, although there were problems particularly with the analysis of the mass of imagery.

An interesting example and a demonstration of an *ad hoc* system put together in quick time, was the use of US Defense Support Programme (DSP) satellites, which were used to detect and locate *Scud* missile launches and to provide likely targets with a few minutes' warning. The DSP satellites were originally intended to detect the launching of Soviet ballistic missiles.

Significant contributions to US space surveillance have been made by the *Big Bird* and *Keyhole* series of satellites. These satellites typically have among their sensor package a general survey camera and a high resolution camera for specific analysis of small sections of the wide angle views. It is likely that these satellites had to be controlled precisely in a sun-synchronous orbit so that they could view the same area at the same lighting conditions each day.

Many claims have been made with respect to the capability of satellite imagery. The resolution of it may be limited by any one of a number of factors. These may include atmospheric effects, satellite stability, satellite telescope quality and sensor detector size and bandwidth. Optimum resolution requires low orbits, which may mean a short satellite lifetime and the fact that the greater part of each orbit is wasted.

Satellites can obviously carry all manner of other sensors, in particular, signals intelligence (SIGINT) collectors, electronic support measure (ESM) systems, locating sensors and multi-frequency radar systems.

While the cost of launching satellites is high, they have such great ability that they are not just the preserve of superpowers. France launched its first military satellite – *Helios* 1A – using the *Arianne* rocket launched from the Kourou space centre in French Guyana.

Commercial satellite imagery is becoming more widely available. In the future the exploitation of commercial data, particularly in preparation for hostilities, will not be preventable without physically destroying the satellite. Thus the destruction of an enemy's airforce may not suffice to deny him vital tactical intelligence, albeit delivered somewhat late.

The French *SPOT* (*Système Probatoire d'Observation de la Terre*) satellites, whose data is commercially available, has a resolution of 10m on the ground, and the Russian DD5 material, again commercially available, has a resolution comparable to a footprint on the ground of approximately 2m. The resolution obtained by military systems cannot be disclosed here, but it may be realistically expected that they would achieve greater levels of resolution than those of the best commercial systems.

Aerial Surveillance

Combat intelligence provided by aircraft is one of the most important inputs to commanders at divisional level and above. The sensor systems include radar, SIGINT collectors and imaging systems.

Radar offers considerable advantages in terms of range and may also operate in poor weather. The theory of radar and in particular the operation of synthetic aperture radar (SAR) is covered in Chapter 7 but the observations which gave rise to the development of a stand-off system are given here.

The width of the radar beam which affects the azimuthal resolution is proportional to the ratio between the wavelength used and the size of the antenna. Good resolution may thus be achieved by operating at very short wavelengths or by using a large antenna. Unfortunately, atmospheric attenuation generally increases with increasing frequency (decreasing wavelength) making it impossible to use wavelengths shorter than the centimetre bands without a considerable reduction in range performance. In the case of airborne installations weight and volume considerations place heavy constraints on antenna size. In an initial attempt to overcome these limitations designers exploited the length of the fuselage by installing the antenna parallel to the length of the aircraft. This meant that an antenna could be used of such a size as to satisfy reasonably normal res-olution requirements. A 5m long antenna operating at a frequency of 10 GHz (a wavelength of 3cm) can provide satisfactory resolution up to a distance of 16–20 miles. The first radar system known as SLAR, side looking airborne radar, was tested in the UK in 1954. Three years later the USAF installed the first operational SLAR and this has been in service on *Phantom* RF-4C for some 25 years. With a radius of action of approximately 1,800km the aircraft is devoid of all armament. In addition to cameras and IRLS the RF-4C carries the APQ-102 SLAR. Current SLARs have a moving target indication (MTI) mode so that any moving targets are displayed and areas of ground may be resolved to approximately 20m × 20m.

The system resolution was obviously limited by antenna length, hence the development of SAR. Until digital technology and integrated circuitry had matured real-time processing was not possible. In 1981 the TR-1 was introduced into service by the USAF. This development of the U2 had optional sensor pack-ages including a SAR. From a height of about 65,000 feet this system was capable of looking approximately 500km deep, thus allowing a stand-off of about 250km and still producing a long-range depth capability.

The perceived lack of depth combat intelligence at army group level and below together with the doctrine of Air Land Battle and Follow on Force Attack spurred the need for more capable systems. The first and by far the most capable was Joint Surveillance Target Attack Radar System (JSTARS).

This is an airborne SAR multimode radar and associated C³ equipment in a converted Boeing 707 E-8A with mobile ground stations to receive the airborne radar data. The radar is designed to overlook the battlefield and areas up to 200km deep, with an approximate 100km stand-off flying at about 40,000 feet. The radar data is passed to ground station modules for processing and dissemi-nation to army commanders. On-board processing to provide target acquisition is carried out so attack aircraft may be tasked. JSTARS can detect and track targets and direct attacks with long-range, ground-based weapons.

Both JSTARS E-8As under test in August 1990 were deployed to the Gulf. They flew near the Kuwait/Iraq border and had considerable success. JSTARS detected the Iraqi build-up leading to the border battle of Khafji.

The UK has also carried out a SAR demonstration programme at both high and low altitudes. The high-altitude demonstration is investigating the potential of SAR to detect and differentiate individual stationary targets such as trucks at ranges of up to 300km. The low-level demonstration is installed in an unpres-surised aircraft operating at altitudes of up to about 10,000 feet. It is probably based on a radar with MTI capability which is able to detect slow-moving ground vehicles and helicopters at ranges of up to approximately 150km.

The French Army has also run the feasibility programme *Orchidee* (*Observative Radar Coherent Heliporte d'Investigation des Elements Ennemis*). The radar is probably a pulse doppler with a mechanically scanned beam antenna mounted under the fuselage of a *Super Puma* helicopter. It will fly between 6,500 and 13,000 feet and will be able to track moving targets up to approximately 150km from the aircraft.

Airborne Early Warning Radar

The air component of an enemy is of great significance. Early warning of enemy air attacks is required in order that they may be engaged and warning given to likely targets. The AWACS (Airborne Warning and Control System) E3A is the most capable current one. It was yet another system which was proved on operations in the Gulf War and its contribution to controlling the air battle to prevent losses among the Coalition air units was significant. The first E3A was produced in 1975, using a Westinghouse APY-1 radar. The aircraft is capable of remaining on station for approximately 6 hours up to 1,000km from its base. The radar looks out from the aircraft some 500km from an operating altitude of about 30,000 feet with a low-altitude range of some 350km. It can also track to an altitude of approximately 80,000 feet. The system has good resistance to jamming.

IMAGING

IRLS and Thermal Imagery

IRLS and thermal imagers (fast framing TIs are often called forward looking infra-red, FLIR) provide thermal pictures of the target area. Both systems are combined in the *Tornado* reconnaissance version and have a considerable capability.

Photography

The importance of photographic reconnaissance has not been diminished by the introduction of other sensors. Panoramic coverage is especially useful for wide field intelligence gathering with high definition and resolution. The development of modern lenses allows the option of extremely long focal lengths and hence high resolutions, but stability and motion blurring tend to limit the focal length to approximately 100cm.

Remotely-Piloted Vehicles

Remotely-piloted vehicles (RPVs) overcome many of the limitations of drones and the vulnerabilities of reconnaissance aircraft. By definition they are remotely controlled by a ground-based or airborne pilot and are consequently able to react to commands in flight usually as a result of information gathered from their own sensors and transmitted over a real-time data link.

Most RPVs used in the surveillance or target acquisition role share basic principles of operation. They are designed to reconnoitre the battlefield to a depth of 50 to 100km, dependent upon whether they are fulfilling the intelligence or fire support requirement. This is a limitation imposed by the need for a simple line-of-sight data link.

They survive primarily by being too small to be tracked by radar or to be hit by a missile. The basic sensor payload is typically a modern CCD TV camera or thermal imager gimballed and stabilised. The data link feeds back to a ground data terminal (GDT). The ground control station (GCS) is usually covered by a three-man crew, a mission controller, pilot and image analyst. The GCS records the RPV's position, which is determined from the beaming of the data link and through information passed down it, with the result that the images are related to a map.

Although the RPV will need to be flown from as far forward as possible, to reduce transit time, fuel and hence all-up mass (AUM), the vulnerability of the ground elements will mean that it is unlikely to be sited closer than 10km from the forward line of own troops (FLOT).

The AUM is one of the most important considerations for an RPV since for a given payload, set by the sensor requirement and engine mass, it imposes a limit on loiter time. It also has an impact on handling. If too large, the launch vehicle becomes heavy and the RPV has to be capable of being dismantled.

The operating height is determined by the ability of the sensor to resolve the fine detail needed for target recognition, the need for a reasonable field of view and the need to maintain communications. Further aspects are cloud cover and cloud base, for the RPV must have a high probability of operating below cloud if its sensors are to be used. Operating height has a bearing on vulnerability and to operate below approximately 300m renders an RPV particularly vulnerable to visual detection and small arms fire.

The choice between fixed and rotary wing tends to be in favour of the fixed wing as its aerodynamic performance is superior, in that it is faster, has greater range and longer loiter time. The rotary wing scores with respect to launch and recovery and may be a better solution for use in battle group or brigade areas.

Data Links

One of the major operational difficulties of the RPV is the maintenance of an unobstructed line of sight between its data link antenna and the GDT. The higher the frequency of this link the more critical is the requirement of an unobstructed path. The choice of frequency is governed by the amount of information that the link is required to carry. TV and FLIR require a broad band or high information rate link and therefore require a higher frequency than IRLS or MTI radar sensors. Clearly the lowest possible frequency consistent with the required data rate should be chosen to reduce this problem. Accidental loss of the link does not necessarily lead to the loss of the RPV as its navigation system can be programmed to initiate emergency action in this eventuality; for example, by returning to the point at which communication was lost or by increasing altitude. A deliberate loss of link might even be operationally desirable on a preprogrammed mission although the loss of real-time sensor information is an obvious disadvantage. It is important that the role of the RPV is clearly defined and that only the sensors required to meet its role are carried.

Elevated Sensors

Several methods of raising sensors above the ground to get a better angle of sight have been tried, for example, balloons and masts. Neither method is without problems of stability and as a consequence some form of movement compensation may be required. Nevertheless masts have been used to elevate *Giraffe* a Swedish air defence surveillance radar with a range of approximately 20–40km and MSTAR on the *Warrior* observation post vehicle (OPV). It is also of note that balloons have been used to good effect; it was a radar mounted on a tethered balloon that first gave warning of the Iraqi invasion of Kuwait.

Tethered platforms have been developed, for example, the *Kiebitz* was a rotor-powered platform on which could be mounted a variety of sensors including radar, LLTV, TI and EW devices. The problem of stabilisation of sensors was overcome and the vehicle could be flown in steady winds up to 15ms^{-1}. *Kiebitz* had an impressive endurance since fuel was supplied to the gas turbine engine through the tether cable which was also used for the transmission of control monitoring and sensor signals. The 8m diameter rotor was driven by compressed air from the rotor tips thus eliminating the need for a tail rotor. The platform was flown at an altitude of 300m which gave the radar a range of about 50km.

The principle drawback of mast-borne or tethered sensors is that they still cannot see into dead ground, wooded areas or towns. Hence their coverage is defective compared with that of a simple RPV.

Remote Ground Sensors

Remote ground sensors (RGS) originally came into service as military intruder alarms such as *TOBIAS*. This simple seismic device, notable for its high false alarm rate, has long been superseded by more reliable sensors employing several detection techniques in a wide range of surveillance applications which are not adequately covered by more conventional means. These include border surveillance, the protection of sensitive installations, route surveillance, the surveillance of dead ground and 'over the hill', encompassing the detection of both ground and airborne targets. Improvements in the ability to discriminate between targets has now led to their being used direct in the fusing systems of mines.

Basic Requirements for an RGS System

The purpose of the system is to detect, locate and (possibly) recognise or identify a target. The fundamental requirement is thus for a simple, reliable device with a low false alarm rate, easy to implant, small enough to prevent easy detection and being either anti-tamper or self destructing. A remote link usable by day and by night and in all weathers, receives the sensor signal, processes it and transmits it to a remote operator. The signal processing must be carried out as a part of the sensing system to reduce the quantity of information to be transmitted; this reduces the transmission bandwidth required. The risk of discovery is lessened by a restricted transmission time so that the sensor should transmit only when a significant event has occurred and might reveal, for example, the number of vehicles forming the target, their speed, direction and type.

The complete system requires a number of such sensors at known positions with each sensor being identified by an electronic coding device. The system may use an 'alerting' sensor and one or more 'confirming' sensors.

The basic technical problem is to identify a characteristic environmental disturbance generated by a target which is detectable at the required range and still retains the identifying features of the disturbance. The effect on the disturbance of the transmitting medium must therefore be considered as well as any relevant background masking signals. The temporal variation and frequency content of the latter are important. The ease with which countermeasures or camouflage may be applied to the target is a further significant factor; this makes acoustic and seismic outputs of particular importance as they are difficult to reduce.

It is essential that the task required of the sensor system should be specified in detail, including:

- the target type and range;
- the target characteristics required;
- topographical factors;
- the likely ambient 'noise'.

The requirements of small size, low power consumption, minimum complexity and cost dictate that the simplest system adequate for a particular task should be used. In addition to a low false alarm rate, any system must be acceptable to the user in the ease of interpreting the sensor outputs into the activity that is actually occurring; a good display is necessary for this, possibly by using sensor-activated lights on a map display.

Sensor Types for an RGS System

In theory any physical change in the environment due to the target may be used for its detection. Commonly used techniques utilise the following target characteristics:

- seismic (ground-borne vibration) disturbance due to movement;
- emission of acoustic waves;
- emission of infra-red radiation;
- changes produced in the local magnetic field.

Seismic Sensing

The energy transferred into the ground by a moving target is propagated over large distances and can be detected by using geophones to convert the vibrations into electrical signals. The simplicity of the geophone system and its low cost and power requirement make this technique the most widely used, particularly in the role of the 'alerting' sensor.

Figure 8.1 shows the geophone structure; movement of the soil in which the geophone is firmly embedded results in relative motion between a magnet attached to the geophone case and a coil suspended on an inertial spring. The resulting induced output voltage is proportional to the relative motion of the

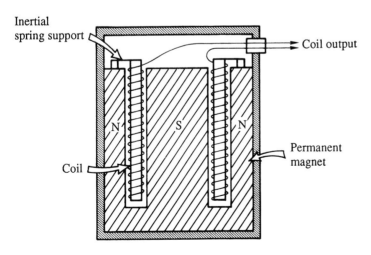

Figure 8.1 Geophone Structure

magnet and the coil and hence to the (vertical) velocity of the ground, and usually varies with frequency. Geophones are commercially used only up to 30 Hz or so as the ground rapidly absorbs higher frequency energy. Higher frequencies can be detected from seismic waves produced close to the sensor, for example, by airborne sound from targets such as helicopters (discussed later).

Transmission in the ground has several effects on the seismic signal apart from the simple spreading out of the energy. Layers of different acoustic properties will make several propagation paths possible due to reflection and refraction. Resonance effects in these layers may amplify some frequencies. All frequencies above 30 Hz are rapidly absorbed by the soil. Thus the received signal may differ considerably from the target signature in both the time and frequency domain, added to which the nature of the ground is critical. It is, however, generally possible to classify targets as wheeled or tracked, and under favourable conditions discrete frequency components can provide recognition.

The main problems are thus:-

- the seismic signal generated by a target may be both complicated and variable;
- the form of the detected signal may change markedly with range, bearing little resemblance to the signal at the source in its variation with time and in frequency content, thus complicating recognition;
- background noise, both natural (especially wind) and man-made, may limit the usable amplification and hence the maximum detection range, and may corrupt the target signature resulting in incorrect target classification or false alarms;
- the geophone will respond to all sources within its detection range, independently of direction of origin.

It may be possible to reduce the noise problem by decreasing the detection range, for example, in short-range route surveillance. A simple combination of geophones can reduce the effect of random background vibrations. One system responds only to moving sources by detecting a change in the order of activation of two geophones, thus discriminating against stationary background sources as well as indicating vehicle direction.

Acoustic Sensing

The airborne acoustic energy radiated by moving targets may easily be detected by concealed microphones. The detection range depends on:

- the source power and frequency content;
- the atmospheric conditions; wind, humidity and temperature gradients;

- the level and frequency content of background noise;
- the microphone sensitivity.

A vehicle gives a complex acoustic signal as it contains many sources of sound. The detailed spectrum depends on the operation of the vehicle so that identification by the examination of particular frequency outputs is difficult. It should, however, be possible to train detecting systems to recognise familiar whines, for instance, which the ear finds useful as discriminants.

Acoustic and Seismic Location (Arrays)

The technique of sound ranging is a well-established means of target acquisition using the time delay between the component microphones of an array as an acoustic wavefront sweeps across it. These delays and the array geometry predict an area within which the source is likely to be located. The uncertainties arise from the deviations from straight-line paths of the energy travelling from source to detector, due to the vagaries of the atmosphere and corresponding variations with time in the local velocity of sound. The seismic version of this technique has the advantage that conditions *en route* beneath the ground are more stable in time, although local variations in velocity from place to place along the propagation path create an alternative problem.

The use of arrays also makes correlation techniques possible, which reduce the contribution of random background noise. In its simplest form, the simultaneous values of the signals from two (or more) sensors at a series of times are multiplied and added. Random noise gives a near zero value for this sum, and the same result usually applies if the signals are arriving at different times. A correct electronic time delay applied to one signal will, however, result in both apparently arriving simultaneously and the summation becomes large. The direction of approach can be calculated from the applied time delay.

One commercial acoustic helicopter detector system uses a cruciform 4m × 4m array, claimed to have an accuracy of 1° at 5km range. Another uses three microphones in a triangular array and is claimed to detect helicopters out to 10–20km, depending on weather conditions, to an accuracy of 2°. It also stores the signatures of 20 helicopter types and can track up to six targets simultaneously.

The USA has an anti-tank submunition which uses an acoustic array (with an infra-red confirmation sensor) to seek vehicle columns.

Acoustic and Seismic Coupling

Figure 8.2 compares the seismic signatures of *Lynx* and *Chinook* helicopters hovering at 30m at a range of 50m. These frequency spectra exhibit discrete peaks

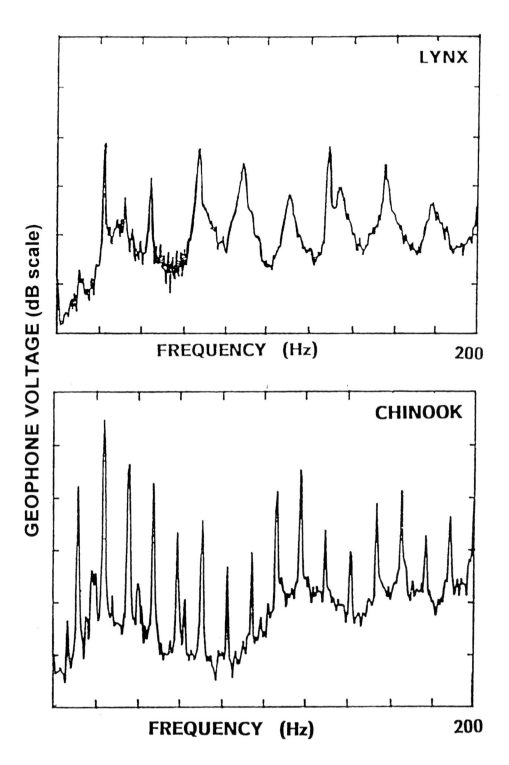

Figure 8.2 Seismic Signature of Lynx and Chinook Helicopters

from the rotors at the blade-passing frequency and the associated harmonics, and provide a clear distinction between the two. The *Lynx* tail rotor is responsible for the 122 Hz peak, indicating that coupling between the airborne sound and the ground takes place at the geophone (coupling at a more distant range, followed by significant ground transmission would have removed such a frequency). This coupling provides a useful extension of the capability of seismic systems to detect airborne targets. Problems due to the frequencies being Doppler-shifted, arising from the movement of the helicopters, may be avoided by examining the ratio of the tail to main rotor frequencies which remains unchanged.

Infra-red Sensing

The normal characteristics of vehicles and men may be used to activate a passive infra-red sensor array. The variation of the signal as the target crosses the field of view of the array can provide identification and direction. The choice of detectors must be such that they require little power and no cooling otherwise the sensor becomes complex and expensive. This generally leads to the selection of thermal detectors for the device but, because these are much less sensitive than photon detectors, the range performance is usually quite short.

Magnetic Field Sensing

The ferromagnetic content of a piece of military equipment produces a small change in the local magnetic field. Several techniques exist for detecting such changes. Detection ranges are not high, a rifle is typically detectable at 2m and a large vehicle at about 30m, depending on the amount of magnetic material present. The simplest detectors tend to be very small and therefore easy to conceal; however, problems remain of background (magnetic) noise – due to power lines or transient natural variations in the local magnetic field – but magnetic sensors make a useful addition to a seismic sensor in confirming the presence of a ferrous-containing target, and the Gulf War re-emphasised the importance of mines (using magnetic fusing) as an effective barrier against mobile armour.

RGS Systems: Current and Future

Depending on the military requirement, there will be varying needs for detection, recognition, identification and location. A specific requirement demands an appropriate choice of sensor as no suitable all-purpose system is possible. A combination of surveillance devices in one sensor head may be useful, with acoustic or seismic sensors acting as inexpensive methods of detecting movement and activating a more sophisticated, and expensive, sensor.

A typical British system provides a seismic and infra-red capability, with personnel/wheeled/tracked vehicle classification and an ability to compare the present and the past activation pattern of eight seismic sensors. A display panel simplifies the interpretation of these changes by indicating the sensor positions on a sketch map of the area under surveillance.

Sensor combinations are also being incorporated direct into fusing systems; for example, in anti-helicopter mines, which clearly emphasises the need for unambiguous target recognition.

Weapon Locating Radars

An important acquisition capability is provided by weapon-locating radars. The technology behind these is covered in Chapter 7. The requirement is demanding in view of the quality and variety of artillery likely to be faced on the modern battlefield and the hostile electronic environment.

SIGINT AND ESM

While in terms of technology SIGINT and ESM systems are outside the scope of this work, nevertheless they are important depth-surveillance and target-acquisition assets. They are either ground- or air-based and are capable of locating radio and radar emitters. Often the characteristics of the emitter are such that its signature can be recognised and, of course, much useful intelligence may be gained by interception of transmissions. Direction finding (DF) techniques can provide acquisition and location for weapons with a large area of engagement, or that can search for and locate their targets once in the general area. DF is also important with respect to cuing fine-grain sensors.

STAY-BEHIND ZONES AND LONG-RANGE RECONNAISSANCE

The concept of well concealed parties providing intelligence or directing fire needs little explanation and is widely used. Such parties are equipped with short-range surveillance devices, and their link back to headquarters is a vital and vulnerable part of the system.

With the advent of the less dense battlefield, long-range ground reconnaissance units will also be able to deploy deep into enemy territory. This is a robust system which is inherently flexible, can carry out on the spot analysis, make value judgements and interpret a commander's intentions.

SUMMARY

While there have been great advances in the technology to make possible depth surveillance and target acquisition, so much so that phrases such as the 'transparent battlefield' have become commonplace, the dispersion of forces and the emphasis on deception still maintain a high level of uncertainty at all levels of command. Counting of individual equipments has become commonplace, but their state and the intention of their commanders are still difficult to discern. Battle damage assessment is difficult yet essential with limited quantities of precision-guided missiles. The requirement to fight a depth battle and the decision making process to do so are deemed essential elements of modern warfare, yet the commanders at corps level and below in most armies are still lacking in resources to generate the information they require to make their decisions.

9

Counter-Surveillance

GENERAL PRINCIPLES

Counter-surveillance (CS) directed against enemy surveillance devices (SD) may have two objectives:

- Negative counter-surveillance aims to frustrate the attempts by the enemy to use his equipment to obtain information of the disposition, movement and tactical activity of his opponents;
- Positive counter-surveillance seeks to inject false information into enemy surveillance devices so that he draws wrong conclusions concerning his opponent's activities and is led into tactical disaster.

In this chapter there will be much contrasting of the action and counter-action of two opposing sides. It will clarify description throughout to maintain Red Land as using surveillance devices and Blue Land who practises counter-surveillance.

If Blue Land is to provide effective CS against Red Land his first requirement is for accurate and timely intelligence so that he knows the spectrum of devices being employed by Red Land and, if possible, the details of the equipment likely to be deployed against him. In the absence of such intelligence, Blue Land must assume the enemy to have a capability at least comparable with his own.

Blue Land must plan to spread his CS resources right across the range of Red Land's surveillance devices to avoid a dangerous gap. For example, there would be little point in camouflaging a missile launcher position against visual observation if the thermal signature of the installation was allowed to remain prominent.

The sudden and obvious use by Blue Land of CS should only be undertaken as a result of a deliberate tactical plan. Such an event would obviously lead Red Land to expect some form of immediate tactical activity. This is, of course, merely an example of the universal concept that in warfare no single aspect of tactical activity must be allowed to be considered in isolation.

Another general consideration is the need to relate each CS technique to its immediate environment. This is obvious when the impact of a jungle camouflage uniform in a snow-covered landscape is considered, but is equally important when the seismic signature of mule transport against a background of modern motor transport is involved. CS also shares, with electronic warfare in general, the need for rapid and flexible response to unexpected situations created by Red Land. The introduction of new equipment or radically new methods of using existing equipment are examples of this.

Finally, the overriding importance of adequate training and self-discipline on the part of Blue Land troops cannot be overemphasised. Even the best CS equipment will be largely ineffective if improperly used.

TECHNIQUES OF COUNTER SURVEILLANCE

The Visual and NIR Region of the EM Spectrum

Most techniques of CS in the visual part of the spectrum are older than war itself. No discussion of CS would, however, be adequate without a short review of the main methods which have been developed over the years. These methods are also an important introduction to techniques used in other parts of the spectrum where the forms of visual CS have their counterparts, in many cases almost exact analogues. The point should be made, however, that a given technique may not have the same importance in different parts of the surveillance spectrum. For example, stand-off jamming (SOJ) is highly effective in the disruption of microwave radar but is much less so in the visual part of the spectrum.

The several visual CS techniques which Blue Land may adopt in order to confuse or deceive the SD of Red Land are discussed below.

The Adoption of Low Profile Movement and Deployment
This technique is nothing more nor less than the intelligent exploitation of the environment and, in particular, the use of ground by the Blue Land commanders. The basic concept is the use of natural features to interrupt the line of sight of the Red Land SDs. Note must also be taken of the fact that moving objects are more readily detected than stationary ones and that regular or highly ordered movement is easier to locate than erratic movement. A dramatic example of the suppression of movement was the 'freezing' of no man's land patrols when star shells were fired during the trench warfare of the First World War.

The well-known scientific fact that regular patterns – in almost any setting – are easier to recognise than irregular shapes or time profiles is now established in military doctrine, although history is rich in examples of the breach of this simple tactical concept. The CS task of avoiding obvious change in successive

Red Land reconnaissance pictures is an example of a particularly difficult problem.

The Use of Camouflage

There are two main aspects of the use of camouflage by Blue Land:

- the task of changing the reflectivity characteristics of elements of his forces to reduce their contrast with the background so as to minimise the chance of detection by Red Land SD;
- to devise methods and equipment to reduce the impact of Blue Land activity on his environment of such a nature as to draw attention to that activity.

The manufacture of 'camouflage nets' which are effective in different situations is a highly skilled engineering technique capable of considerable further development, particularly when the need to camouflage at all frequencies of the EM spectrum is considered. The ease with which a reflective covering can be deployed or packed for movement is of considerable importance.

Damage to vegetation and ground by Blue Land units in motion, particularly heavy vehicles, is difficult to conceal. A more fruitful approach may well be to hide the movement of important military units among the normal flow of routine traffic. This is much easier to achieve on hard roads and in built-up areas. A particularly interesting example of this type of CS was the proposal by the USA to conceal the whereabouts of its MX missile by an entirely artificial environment which does not change when the missile is present and possible deployment among normal traffic on the continental railroad network in times of tension.

The tendency of all human beings to walk the shortest distance possible is likely to produce highly characteristic weapon site signatures if track discipline is not firmly enforced.

The MIR and the FIR Region of the EM Spectrum

The general concepts explained above are just as applicable to this region of the EM spectrum. The major difference being in the self-generation of black-body radiation from the objects rather than reflected energy.

In general, Blue Land units and personnel will be at a higher temperature than the background and will therefore exhibit a positive thermal contrast. Several areas can be considered in attempting to reduce this contrast:

- the use of low emissivity coatings (care must be taken with this concept as too low an emissivity will mean a high reflectivity);

- thermal insulation of hot spots;
- forced air cooling;
- exhaust plume management.

The Use of Barriers and Decoys

The use of smoke screens to avoid visual observation has been used for centuries. In its modern form the rapid deployment of smoke by projectors is an important part of the self-defence armoury of Blue Land forces seeking to avoid observation by Red Land SDs. It must be remembered, however, that although smoke may be highly effective against visual observation it is technically much more difficult to produce smoke barriers which are effective against FIR systems or even longer wavelength devices. This is because of the need to employ larger and larger suspended particles as the wavelength of concern is increased. Such large particles tend to sink through the air quickly, making the production of persistent smoke clouds difficult. Research into multi-waveband smokes continues apace in several countries.

The use by Blue Land of decoys includes the normal tactical ploy of 'creating a diversion' which requires the use of normal forces and equipment to act as decoys. However, specially constructed equipment may also be used, particularly to effect positive CS against Red Land reconnaissance pictures. Such devices may consist of two- or three-dimensional models of the vehicles or equipment to be represented. Again it must be remembered that a dummy unit of this type may need to be provided with fake communication transmissions if the Red Land force supports reconnaissance sensors with electronic support measures (ESM). The decoys may also have to be provided with credible signatures in the appropriate wavebands; for example, thermal emission characteristics. As with all other aspects of military hardware, the impact of modern technology is such as to make everything much more costly.

It should be noted that 'simple' decoys were used to great effect in the Falklands War, and by both sides in the Gulf War (Iraqi units burned oil drums on the backs of fully operational tanks to fool aerial surveillance devices, and the American Secretary of Defense, William Perry, is quoted as saying, 'We spent a lot of time and energy blowing up dummy *Scuds*').

THE PHYSICAL DESTRUCTION OF SURVEILLANCE DEVICES

Given the fact that Blue Land knows the location of the Red Land's SDs, then the use of normal weapons to destroy those SD or the men who operate them is an obvious option for Blue Land forces. In the visual region the SD will in most cases be the human eye aided by optical instruments. In the majority of circumstances the Red Land visual and infra-red SDs will be passive (i.e., they will not need to illuminate their targets) and their location may be in doubt. Where large SD installations are involved, Blue Land may resort to raiding parties to destroy such installations *in situ*. In such a case expert advice and training should be available to ensure that permanent damage may be inflicted as economically as possible and that the same damage is inflicted on like installations so that subsequent cannibalisation by Red Land may be frustrated.

In the tradition of the tactic of throwing sand into the eyes of the enemy, there is current interest in the development of weapons specifically designed to destroy optical (visual and infra-red) surveillance devices.

Dazzle and Damage Laser Weapons

There has been much discussion in the press of laser weapons of such power that they are capable of causing physical damage to strategic missile and other types of weapon. These are by their very nature subject to understandable security classification and it would be pointless to discuss such matters further.

However, it may readily be derived from information freely available in any physics laboratory that if a visual or IR system is able to operate by reflected or radiated energy from a target, then a laser located at or near that target and operating at the same optical wavelength would be able to direct energy of such a level as to dazzle or damage the detector, whether the human eye or a semiconductor device. Clearly the power level required of the laser would be much less to dazzle a detector than to damage it. The Soviet Navy is alleged to have tested such a laser weapon against an American P-3 *Orion* maritime patrol aircraft which was carrying out routine reconnaissance of Soviet vessels on exercise.

Surveillance system protective devices intended to minimise the effects of dazzle and damage lasers would obviously be called for in the specification of any optical or IR device used for surveillance. The existence and performance of such lasers or their counter-counter-devices would be closely guarded national secrets.

The Use of Nuclear Devices

If the type of warfare being waged by Blue Land and Red Land includes the use of nuclear weapons the vulnerability of Red Land SD to nuclear attack must be considered. The normal effects of the blast, heat flash and radiation will affect Red Land surveillance devices as they will affect any other equipment. In addition to this, Red Land surveillance devices are likely to contain electronic signal processing circuits which would be particularly susceptible to any large EM fields or nuclear particle flux which might be created by Blue Land or indeed Red Land, nuclear explosions. The hardening of electronic equipment against this type of attack is a highly specialised subject which will not be pursued here.

Retroreflective Protective Barriers and Dazzle Sources

There is plenty of historical evidence that the tactical use of the sun as a means of dazzling the enemy has been employed for a long time. There have been accounts of armies who have used highly polished shields to reflect the image of the sun into the faces of advancing enemy forces.

The extension of such concepts by Blue Land to produce artificial sources of light or retroreflective shields to throw back the light must certainly be considered. However, there is little unclassified published material on the current use of such systems, which must therefore be considered speculative at present.

Where Red Land employs image intensifiers, however, it is probable that Blue Land could employ light sources of sufficient power which would cause such systems to overload and thus fail to function properly.

SUMMARY OF OPTICAL CS EQUIPMENT

To summarise, it may be said that, in spite of the counter-optical techniques that have evolved over centuries of warfare, modern armies have little CS equipment for use in the visual region in general use. Their normal equipment is likely to be confined to camouflage and smoke-producing devices. It remains to be seen whether the dazzle and damage laser will produce a significant change in the future.

COUNTER-SURVEILLANCE TECHNIQUES AGAINST COMMUNICATIONS ESM

The extensive use of EM telecommunications by all modern armies has led to a massive effort being put into surveillance devices which are effectively ESM receiving systems directed against telecommunication transmitters. Thus Red Land would deploy ESM facilities which would not only monitor messages transmitted by Blue Land, with the hope of decoding them and obtaining their actual meaning, but also would determine the signature and location of each transmitter with the intent of discerning some meaningful tactical pattern. Blue Land would assume that such activity was in progress and might well go to considerable lengths to inject false information into the Red Land system. This action and counteraction is the essence of communications electronic warfare and the reader is directed to *Communications and Information Systems for Battlefield Command and Control* by M A Rice and A J Sammes for further discussion of this vitally important aspect of modern war.

TECHNIQUES OF CS AGAINST MEDIUM-LEVEL SURFACE-TO-AIR RADAR

The Problem

Medium-level, surface-to-air radars in the land force context are usually associated with anti-aircraft weapon systems. We are not here concerned with the counter systems operating against the surveillance elements of them. Such systems currently deployed usually use missiles rather than guns and are typified by the American *Improved Hawk* equipment or the Russian SA6 mobile units.

For the purposes of this discussion we must consider the use by Blue Land of CS to protect its aircraft against observation by Red Land's medium anti-aircraft radar (MAR) which corresponds in role (but not in its hypothetical performance) to the *Improved Hawk* pulse acquisition radar (PAR) or the Russian *Flatface* Radar.

It is convenient to make some hypothetical assumptions about the performance of Red Land MAR, representing existing in-service technology. It is assumed to be a low PRF single-beam radar with a good detection performance against small aircraft out to 100km range and 30km height. The beam sweeps a complete azimuth circle in eight seconds.

Moving target indication (MTI) circuits are available to the operators who also have at their disposal certain anti-jamming facilities – unknown in detail to Blue Land at the outbreak of hostilities. It is further assumed that information is obtained from the radar by operators observing targets on plan position indicator (PPI) displays. The pulse length of the radar is 4μs giving a range cell of about 600m length at all ranges. A half-power beamwidth in azimuth of 4° (70 mils) gives a resolution width in azimuth of 700m at the maximum range of 100km. In order to avoid ambiguous range problems, the pulse repetition frequency of the radar may be taken as 1,000 pulses per second or slower.

Faced with a number of Red Land surface-to-air weapon systems equipped with such a radar, Blue Land may adopt several counter-surveillance activities. The first and most obvious is for Blue Land aircraft to fly fast and low, thus denying the Red Land radar clear sight lines and hiding the aircraft echoes in ground clutter. The effectiveness of this tactic will, of course, depend on the potency of the Red Land low-level air defence.

Destruction of the Medium Anti-Aircraft Radars

The powerful transmissions of the MAR will enable Blue Land ESM receivers to locate their position and the accuracy of the location can, if necessary, be enhanced by the use of additional sensors. Airborne ESM equipment will be the most effective and flexible, but ground-based equipment may also be used –

particularly if high ground overlooking the MAR positions is available. The signature of the MAR will be highly characteristic and the Blue Land ESM installations should have little difficulty in identifying them. Conditions on the battlefield may result in a very high density of pulses of EM radiation so that modern ESM systems may well be capable of intercepting and processing up to a million pulses per second.

The Blue Land task of location will be made more difficult if the Red Land MAR have facilities for frequency agility, variable PRF and adaptable pulse length. Once the positions of the Red Land MAR have been pinpointed they may be attacked by any of the usual weapons, including anti-radiation, passive homing missiles which may be either air- or surface-launched.

Passive Jamming and Decoys

The use of passive jamming has been employed since the early days of radar. The usual method is to distribute clouds of chaff, also known as 'window', which consists of thin strips of aluminium cut to such a length as to produce a large reflection of the radar pulses. Blue Land could 'sow' chaff clouds from aircraft specially employed for the task or might use chaff shells or rockets.

The chaff clouds persist for quite long periods as the individual strips fall slowly. The clouds move with the air that supports them and may cause general confusion to Red Land operators. However, the use of MTI by Red Land would greatly reduce the effectiveness of chaff. It will also be clear that the use of chaff in this type of engagement would require a carefully prepared Blue Land plan. It would be of little or no value for the protection of an isolated aircraft against observation by a MAR.

Other forms of decoy involving the launch of relatively expensive airborne vehicles with specially enhanced radar echoing area may also be used in carefully preplanned set-piece attacks by Blue Land, but it is unlikely that such a method would be used for routine tactical warfare or reconnaissance parties by individual aircraft.

Reduction of Radar Cross Section

If the operating frequency of the Red Land MAR may be assumed at the time of the development of the Blue Land aircraft, much can be done to reduce the radar cross-section (RCS) – or echoing area. The strength of the echo returned by a passive target such as an aircraft will depend upon its shape, the material of which it is made, and its aspect with respect to the MAR illuminating beam. In the past the design of the airframe and engines of aircraft has been dominated by aerodynamic considerations so that the reduction of RCS has been a matter of modifying the aircraft by minor shaping and the application of low-reflective covering to selected areas at a later stage. However, the vital importance of low RCS to the survival of military aircraft is now fully appreciated so that consideration is given to this aspect of design right from the start, even though this must mean a reduction in performance in some other aspects.

The development of radar absorbent material (RAM) and anti-reflectant paint has been in progress for many years and several firms will supply them. However, this is another example of an area where detailed information is both difficult to obtain and sensitive. This is also true of progress made in the performance of systems which seek to reduce target signatures by taking in the radar pulse by special antenna, amplifying it, inverting its phase, and transmitting it back towards the radar so that the retransmitted pulse tends to cancel the pulse reflected from the skin of the target. This type of equipment, which may be regarded as a form of active jammer, could only be carried at the expense of other payloads.

Publicity given in the USA to the concept of the 'stealth' type of fighter and strategic bomber tends to emphasise the importance attached to the reduction of the RCS of strategic and tactical vehicles. For example, the RCS of a B-52 is approximately $100m^2$, whereas that of the B-2 stealth bomber is approximately $0.1m^2$, and that of the F117 stealth fighter is only $0.025m^2$. Once again a Gulf War example is the extremely effective use made of the F117 stealth fighters which destroyed the Iraqi airforce headquarters without anyone even knowing they were in the vicinity.

The Use of Active Jammers to Defeat Medium Anti-Aircraft Radar

There are a number of different types of jammer which may be directed against a MAR and these must first be identified. The best and most effective jamming for Blue Land to use will depend upon a number of factors which relate to the actual conflict under consideration. The first classification concerns the type of platform which carries the jammer. If the target itself carries the jammer it is described as a target borne jammer (TBJ) or an airborne self-protection jammer (ASPJ). If another Blue Land aircraft – dedicated to jamming – provides jamming support for the target it will be called a stand-off jammer (SOJ) if it is further away from the victim MAR than the target it is trying to hide. If the jamming aircraft is close to the target it is called an escort jammer (EJ), while a supporting jammer flying close to its victim is called a stand-in jammer (SIJ).

The SIJ does not require very high jamming power because it is beaming its power into the Red Land radar aerial at short range. It must however adopt a 'loiter' flight path in the field of view of the victim radar. It is therefore likely to be a small, cheap, remotely-piloted vehicle (RPV) which may well be provided with a small warhead capable of destroying the radar as a 'farewell gesture' when its fuel becomes exhausted.

The escort jamming aircraft, as it must remain close to the aircraft which it is protecting, is likely to be one with a similar performance to the target's. The SOJ, on the other hand, must stay on station behind the target aircraft for some time – probably in a racetrack-shaped flight path. It is jamming from long range and must therefore provide considerable jamming power, probably fed into large, fairly narrow beam aerials. Such aircraft do not need high performance but they should have long endurance and large load-carrying ability.

Any of these jamming platforms may use either noise jamming or deception jamming.

Noise Jamming

Noise jamming is obtained by modulating a powerful transmitter, operating on the same frequency as the Red Land MAR, with random signal fluctuations similar to those which cause random noise. In automatic radars this produces continual false alarms while display radars show a confusing PPI covered with fluctuating 'speckles'. If the Blue Land jammers are fitted with ESM receivers the noise carriers can be tuned to the exact frequency of the victim radars; but if they are 'blind' jammers the carrier of the jammer must be swept to and fro over the expected frequency band. Such swept jammers are less effective than the spot frequency type and partly for this reason many modern radars are frequency agile, that is the carrier frequency is changed in a random fashion from pulse to pulse. This reduces the efficiency even of those jammers provided with listening ESM receivers.

Deception Jamming

There are many types of deception jammer but the majority of them consist of a system which receives the transmitted pulse of the victim radar with a suitable ESM receiver. The pulse is then amplified and transmitted at an artificially delayed time. This gives the Red Land operator a false target on his display at a range or position which differs from that of the real target. In some cases many false returns may be transmitted by the jammer which fills the Red Land display with false targets. Such a jammer is termed a reverberation jammer.

Tactical Location of Jammers

In most circumstances the most effective form of jamming against a Red land MAR type radar would be a 'circus' of SOJs placed by Blue Land behind the attacking aircraft which were being concealed from detection. Such jamming – probably powerful noise jamming – should be positioned on the line extending from the position of the MAR through the location of the Blue Land attacking aircraft. Such a set-piece attack by Blue Land would require careful planning with previous reconnaissance of the location of the Red Land radars and the carrier frequencies likely to be used.

TECHNIQUES OF CS AGAINST LOW-LEVEL SURFACE-TO-AIR RADAR

Surface-to-air radars intended for the detection and location of low-flying aircraft, which must be considered to include both cruise missiles and small unmanned aircraft, are usually directly associated with the weapon systems designed to attack such vehicles. The parameters of these low-level radars (LLR) are quite different from those of the MAR because they must be able to operate against fast, low-flying aircraft which, in a ground environment, may 'unmask' at a very short range and remain in view of the radar for a few seconds only. Also the radar is subject to extensive ground clutter. These circumstances demand a radar with a high pulse-repetition frequency so that blind approach velocities may be avoided, a pulse Doppler form of signal processing so that good performance in heavy clutter may be achieved, a high rotation speed for the antenna which produces a high data rate, and automatic alarm and weapon activation to avoid human slowness of reaction and tendency to fatigue. On the other hand, long range of detection is not required; a maximum of the order of 15km is typical. Faced with such a surveillance device the Blue Land force would provide CS equipment intended to protect its low-flying aircraft from attack by the weapon system directed by the Red Land LLR. The geometrical configuration of this type of situation does not lend itself to the SOJ since the long-range lines of sight are unlikely to exist. However, the automatic detection and essentially rapid response of the LLR lays it open to saturation by false alarms created by noise jamming from short range. Such jamming will, of course, alert the radar that an attack is probable, but the excessive false alarm rate will prevent reliable location of the attacking aircraft. The platforms available to Blue Land from which this noise jamming may be directed include an ASPJ pod on the attacking aircraft, a presensor RPV which may be either ground-launched or drop-launched from Blue Land aircraft, or a short-duration 'dump jammer' delivered by surface-to-surface projectile or rocket.

Such elaborate CS activity on the part of Blue Land may seem excessively costly but it must be remembered that ground-attack aircraft at present under development may well cost the equivalent of $50 million each. Extension of their useful life by protection plans for each sortie may therefore be worthwhile. Where Blue Land is proposing to mount a 'stream' attack by a number of aircraft, anti-radiation missiles (ARMs) which home on to Red Land's LLR may well be launched by the leading planes.

THE FUTURE

A rapid increase in all forms of optical, infra-red and radar sensors on the battle-field has continued over the last few years and shows every sign of even greater expansion in the future.

This means that to pursue a military campaign against an increasingly well equipped enemy with more able surveillance devices will necessitate the development of better and better counter-surveillance techniques. Owing to the very nature of the field of counter-surveillance, much of a nation's technology and capability in this area is shrouded in secrecy; however, it may be expected that as each new surveillance device is introduced on to the battlefield a counter to it will not be far behind.

Glossary of Terms and Abbreviations

A

A_e	Affective radiating aperture of an antenna.
Aerosols	Airborne suspended solid particles or liquid droplets affecting transmission of electro-magnetic energy.
AGC	Automatic gain control.
Ambient	Prevailing background conditions, as in ambient illumination or temperature.
AN/TPQ-37	An example of a phased-array weapon locating radar.
APC	Armoured personnel carrier.
Area of interest	That area of concern to the commander, including the area in which he is capable of directly influencing operations, the area adjacent on the flanks and extending forward to current and future objectives, and the areas occupied or which could be occupied by enemy forces that might affect current or future operations.
ARM	Anti-radiation missile.
ASPJ	Airborne self-protection jammer.
AUM	All-up mass.
AWACS	Airborne early warning control system.

B

B	Receiver bandwidth.
Bandwidth – laser	The wavelength (or frequency) range within the $1/e$ or $1/e^2$ power or energy limits.

Beam divergence	The increase in a laser beam width with range related to specific points where the intensity has fallen to 1/e or $1/e^2$ of the central peak intensity of a gaussian shaped beam.
Beam expander	(Context – laser). A combination of optical elements within the laser system which is used to change the shape of the beam e.g., to increase its diameter whilst decreasing beam divergence.
Beam width – laser	Defined in the ideal case of a gaussian shaped beam as the distance between two directly opposite points at which the intensity has fallen to 1/e or $1/e^2$ of the central peak intensity.
BFA	Beat frequency amplifier – used as baseband amplifier in Doppler systems.
Blindfire	Version of Rapier that uses radar command guidance.
Boresight	Pointing direction of an antenna.
BSR	Battlefield surveillance radar.

<u>C</u>

c	The velocity of electromagnetic radiation in free space – value 3×10^8 m/s.
C	Contrast.
C_1	First radiation constant.
C_2	Second radiation constant.
CCD	Charge coupled device. Solid-state electronic device for storing and/or transferring electric charges, used as solid-state imager or for data transfer.
CLOS	Command to line of sight.
CMT	Cadmium mercury telluride.
CRT	Cathode ray tube – a display device used in television monitors, and in radar displays.
CS	Counter surveillance.
CW	Continuous wave. A CW laser has an output that is continuous and unmodulated.

D

Dark Adaptation	The state of an observer's night vision, or the process of gradually increasing sensitivity to full night vision.
d_{az}	Cross-range resolution as defined for a SAR.
dB	Decibel – a logarithmic scale used for expressing power ratios.
d_{el}	Range resolution as defined for a SAR.
Detection	The discovery by any means of the presence of something of potential military interest.
DF	Direction finding.
DFWES	Direct fire weapon effects simulator.

E

e	The irrational number 2.71828 used as the base of Napier's system of logarithms (natural logarithms).
EBI	Equivalent background illuminance.
E_g	Band gap energy of photon detector.
$E_i(n)$	Integration efficiency for n pulses.
EJ	Escort jammer.
EM	Electromagnetic.
EMS	Electromagnetic spectrum.
E NOHD	Extended nominal ocular hazard distance. The increase over the NOHD due to the use of magnifying optics eg. binoculars.
ESM	Electronic support measure.
EW	Electronic warfare.
Exit pupil	The area outside (behind) the final viewing lens of an optical system where the light is most concentrated. It is thus the optimum position for the viewer's eye-pupil.
Eye relief	The distance between the final viewing lens and the exit pupil (i.e. optimum viewing distance from the instrument).

F

FAR	False alarm rate – the rate at which a radar signals internal noise spikes as targets.
Far-field	The distance beyond the near-field where the laser beam begins to diverge.
f_d	Doppler shift, caused by target motion towards, or away from, the radar.
FIR	Far infra-red, 6 to 15µm.
FLIR	Forward looking infra-red.
FLOT	Forward line of own troops.
f_r	Pulse repetition frequency – the number of pulse per second transmitted by a pulse radar.
FST	Future soviet tank.

G

G	Antenna gain.
GaAs	Gallium Arsenide. Semiconductor material useful as near-IR source for IR illumination or laser. Also used in modern (Generation 3) intensifiers as photocathode material.
Gas Laser	A laser in which the active medium is a gas, and stimulated emission is derived from atomic (e.g., helium-neon), ionic (e.g., argon or krypton) or molecular (e.g., carbon dioxide) transitions.
Gaussian distribution	Also known as a *normal* distribution. It describes a distribution of collectable data that exhibits a symmetrical bell-shaped form.
GCS	Ground control station.
GDT	Ground data terminal.
GHz	Gigahertz – a frequency of 1000 Megahertz (10^9 Hz).

H

h	Planck's constant.

I

Identification	The stage in the acquisition process at which the target is established as being friend or foe and its type.
IF	Intermediate frequency.
IFF	Identification friend or foe – use of secondary radar in air defence.
II	Image intensifier.
I^2R	Imaging infra-red.
InGaAs	Indium Gallium Arsenide. Gallium Arsenide doped with Indium to provide extended near-IR response as a photocathode material.
IR	Infra-red.
IRLS	Infra-red line scan.
IRST	Infra-red search & track.
ISIT	Intensified silicon intensified target, ultra-sensitive low-light TV sensor.

J

JSTARS	Joint surveillance target attack radar system.
JT	Joule Thomson.

K

k	Boltzmann's constant.

L

LADAR	Laser detection & ranging. Refers to cases where the phase (coherence) of a laser beam is employed in heterodyning operations.
Lambertian Surface	Any (matt) surface which appears equally bright from any direction. A useful model for many real surfaces which approximate this behaviour.
LASER	Light amplification by stimulated emission of radiation. A device which produces an intense, coherent, beam of radiation.

Laser doppler heterodyning	A technique used for target ranging and velocity evaluation which makes use of the phase of the laser beam as well as its intensity. It is analogous to microwave heterodyning but offers higher resolution.
LCS	Ladar cross section. Analogous to radar cross section.
LED	Light emitting diode, solid-state device used in displays or as an active light source.
LHAT	Laser hazard area trace. A term used in probabilistic laser safety modelling to describe the area inside which the risk of ocular damage is unacceptable.
LIDAR	Light detection and ranging. Strictly refers to the use of non-coherent sources.
Liquid laser	A laser in which the active medium is a liquid e.g., organic dye.
LLR	Low-level radars.
LLTV	Low-light television.
Location	The determination of a target's position with sufficient accuracy to allow a successful engagement.
LOSBR	Line of sight beam riding.
LPF	Low pass filter.

M

Mach no.	Velocity in terms of the speed of sound.
MAR	Medium anti-aircraft radar.
Martello	Modern British long-range air defence radar.
MBT	Main battle tank.
MCP	Micro-channel plate. The wafer-thin amplification section of Generation 2 image intensifiers
Merlin	Smart mortar round, incorporating a mmW active seeker for terminal homing.
Mie Scattering	Efficient scattering of electromagnetic energy by

particles or droplets of size similar to the radiation wavelength.

milliradian	Mathematical unit of angle, equal to one thousandth of a radian, i.e. 0.057 degrees.
mils	Military unit of angle or elevation. Defined as 1/6400 of a complete rotation (i.e. 0.056 degrees), and for small angles approximated well by height (in m)/Range(in km). One mil is very nearly equal to one milliradian.
MIR	Middle infra-red, 3 to 6μm.
MLRS	Multiple launch rocket system.
MOVL	Minimum ophthalmoscopically visible lesion. Use in probabilistic modelling to describe an acceptable minimum level of eye damage, which can be measured by an ophthalmoscope.
MPE	Maximum permissable exposure.
MSTAR	Man-portable surveillance & target acquisition radar.
MTF	Modulation transfer function. A graph for assessing overall image quality.
MTI	Moving target indication – a technique used in air defence surveillance radars for rejecting stationary clutter.

N

Near-field	The distance from the laser cavity where the beam is highly collimated, essentially parallel, the length of which depends upon the characteristics of the laser.
NIR	Near infra-red, 0.7 to 3μm.
NOHD	Nominal ocular hazard distance.

O

Objective lens	The primary image-forming lens, nearest to the object being viewed.
OPV	Observation post vehicle.

P

PAR	Pulse acquisition radar.
P_{av}	Average transmitter power – the radar output power averaged over the full pulse repetition interval.
PAVE PAWS	Modern ballistic missile early warning radar.
PC	Photo-conductive.
P_d	Probability of detection of the target by a radar system.
Photocathode	Sensitive surface in intensifiers (etc.) responsible for converting incoming light photons into free electrons (photoelectrons).
Photoelectron	Electron set free by photoemission.
Photoemission	The process whereby the impact of incoming light photons ejects free electrons from the body of a metallic or quasi-metallic material (in a photocathode), as used in image intensifiers.
Photon	Single burst of localised electromagnetic wave energy making up visible light flow etc.
Photon noise	Image noise caused by statistical fluctuations in the photon-count in low-light images.
Photopic vision	Daylight vision as opposed to (scotopic) night vision.
Pixel	Single element of a picture made up from individual samples of the image, either in a video camera or digital display.
Population Inversion	A situation where a higher energy state is more populated than a lower energy state.
PPI	Plan position indicator – the standard style of display used in surveillance radars.
PRF	Pulse repetition frequency (same as f_r – both are used in the literature).
P_t	Transmitter peak power – the power output of a radar during the transmitted pulse.
Pulsed laser	A laser that generates energy in pulses rather than continuously.

Pump	A laser energy source (eg. flash lamp) necessary for amplification in the active medium of the laser.
PV	Photo-voltaic.

Q

Quantised	Divided into distinct entities or steps. Light is quantised as its energy is divided up into a series of localised, individual photons.
Q-switched laser	Describes a process where laser emission is prevented, by a shutter-like process, until the state of population inversion has built up to such a degree that upon opening the shutter a very high power pulse is obtained.

R

r	Surface reflectivity.
R	Range.
ΔR	Range resolution of a radar system – represents the minimum spacing in range that two targets can have and still be seen by the radar as separate targets.
RAM	Radar absorbent material.
Rapier	Short-range air defence missile.
Rayleigh scattering	The small amount of scattering produced by airborne particles much smaller than the radiation wavelength.
RCS	Radar cross section.
Recognition	The classification of an object of potential military interest by its appearance or behaviour.
Retina	The light-sensitive layers of cells at the back of the eye which convert incoming light into nerve signals.
RGS	Remote ground sensors.
Rhodopsin	The photochemical in the eye's rod cells responsible for night vision.
R_{mu}	The maximum unambiguous range of a pulse radar – at ranges longer than this the echo returns after the trans-

mission of the next pulse, producing 'second time around echoes'.

RPV	Remotely piloted vehicle.

S

S-25	Photocathode material used in Generation 2 image intensifiers.
SAL	Semi-active laser homing.
SAR	Synthetic aperture radar.
Scotopic vision	Night vision as opposed to daylight. Note that the response of the eye to different wavelengths differs between the two conditions.
SD	Surveillance device.
Semiconductor laser	A laser in which the active medium is a semiconductor material and lasing takes place at the p–n junction eg. Gallium Arsenide (GaAs), also referred to as an injection laser.
SIGINT	Signals intelligence.
SIJ	Stand-in jammer.
SLAR	Side looking airborne radar.
SOJ	Stand-off jamming/jammer.
Solid-state laser	A laser in which the active medium is an atom or an ion which is embedded in a solid host lattice eg. Nd:YAG in which the active medium is triply charged ionic neodymium (Nd^{+3}) in the host Yttrium Aluminium Garnet (YAG, $Y_3Al_5O_{12}$).
SP	Self-propelled gun.
SPRITE	Signal processing in the element.
Stimulated emission	The process by which the emission of laser energy (a photon) from a higher energy state to a lower energy state in an atom, ion or molecule is stimulated by an input radiation (photon) which has identical characteristics (wavelength, phase, polarisation) to the stimulated

photon. The resulting two photons are in phase, constituting amplification.

Surveillance · The continuous systematic watch over the battlefield area.

T

T · Pulse repetition interval in a pulse radar – the time from the beginning of one pulse to the beginning of the next.

Target acquisition · The detection, recognition, identification and location of a target to permit the effective deployment of weapons.

TBJ · Target borne jammer.

TEA laser · Transversely excited atmospheric laser. A (carbon dioxide) laser in which the excitation of the active gas medium is at right angles to the gas flow, producing good output beam quality.

TEM · Transverse electric and magnetic.

TEM_{00} mode · The fundamental or basic mode of oscillation in the laser cavity. The emitted energy or power distribution is gaussian in shape and there is no higher order mode structure.

TI · Thermal imager/imaging.

TWT · Travelling wave tube – a microwave amplifying device frequently used in modern pulse Doppler radars.

U

UAV · Unmanned aerial vehicle.

V

Visibility · A colloqial term often used for visual range.

Visual Acuity · The ultimate resolution capability of the eye, expressed as the reciprocal of the angle subtended by the smallest discernable pattern. When looking at repetitive bar-charts, this is measured in cycles per milliradian.

Visual Range · The range at which atmospheric transmission conditions cause highly contrasted objects to be indistinguishable from their background.

W

W   Radiant emittance.

X

XIR   Extreme infra-red, 15 to 1000μm.

Symbols

α Atmospheric attenuation, (in Radar – usually expressed in dB/km two-way).

ε Surface emissivity.

λ Wavelength.

λ_c Long wavelength cut-off limit for a photon detector.

σ Stefan-Boltzmann's constant. (Context – Infra-red).

           Radar cross-section. (Context – Radar).

θ_B Antenna beamwidth.

θ_s Beamwidth of synthesised beam for a SAR.

τ Pulse width – typically around 1μS in a simple pulse radar.

           Time delay (scan and electrical) in serial scan system (context – infra-red).

Bibliography

Accetta J S & Shumaker D L, *The Infrared and Electro-Optical Systems Handbook*, SPIE (1993)

Barton D K, *Modern Radar Systems Analysis*, Artech House (1988)

Gopel W (editor), *Sensors Vol. 6 "Optical Sensors"*, VCH (1992)

Gregory R L , *Eye and Brain,* Weidenfield & Nicholson (1977)

Kingsley S P & Quegar S, *Understanding Radar Systems*, McGraw-Hill (1992)

Lloyd J M, *Thermal Imaging Systems*, Plenum (1975)

Ristic L (editor), *Sensor Technology and Devices,* Artech House (1994)

Shaw D F (editor) *Information Sources in Physics, 3rd Ed.*, Bowker Saur (1994)

Shimoda K, *Introduction to Laser Physics, 2nd Ed.*, Springer (1991)

Siegman A E, *Lasers*, Univ. Science (1986)

Skolnik M I, *Introduction to Radar Systems*, McGraw-Hill (1981)

Index